THE COMMUNITY OF MAN

THE MACMILLAN COMPANY
NEW YORK · BOSTON · CHICAGO
DALLAS · ATLANTA · SAN FRANCISCO

MACMILLAN AND CO., LIMITED
LONDON · BOMBAY · CALCUTTA
MADRAS · MELBOURNE

THE MACMILLAN COMPANY
OF CANADA, LIMITED
TORONTO

THE COMMUNITY

OF

MAN

HUGH MILLER

New York

THE MACMILLAN COMPANY

1·9·4·9

Copyright, 1949, by THE MACMILLAN COMPANY

First Printing

CONTENTS

* 1 *

REORIENTATION

THIS century has seen incredible things, things incalculable, the prophecy of which would have been thought madness. Whole peoples have gone berserk, the earth has been devastated by global wars, continents lie desolate. Still worse calamity is feared. It is conceivable that war should apply weapons able to destroy all human life, or even the life of this planet. We have entered a new and terrible dimension of being.

As we gaze upon this scene, at first sight chaotic, we begin to discern its pattern. Several centuries of industrialization have steadily transformed the human economy, bringing the peoples of the globe into economic interdependence. This development disturbed the political boundaries which parceled humanity into many small economies, each relatively self-sufficient. People became increasingly aware that political and economic institutions are interrelated, and that the movement to world economy must either be stopped and turned back, or be given its own living conditions by the advance to world polity of some kind.

Religious, national, class, and other group loyalties affected by this political movement were thereby stimulated to intense reaction, intended either to prevent this passage to world economy and world polity or to direct it to a certain goal. Those who actively espoused the movement divided into two factions, advancing alternative programs

[1]

based on opposed conceptions of justice and buttressed by two incompatible philosophies of nature and man. One faction would establish political economy upon property rights inherent in the individual; the other would recognize only communal rights. Two different religious, philosophical, and intellectual traditions came into conflict in this head-on collision between individualistic and collectivistic ideals. Each faction now sees in the other its antithesis, its mortal enemy, something heretical and profoundly immoral. Neither finds in the other anything universal and humanitarian, each sees in the moral pretensions of the other only a cloak for aggressive imperialism. Yet is it not a tremendous achievement of the human reason that men should at last demand the establishment of society and government upon reason? Is it tragedy, or providence in disguise, that lets man's effort to be rational produce not one rational faith, but two apparently incompatible faiths?

The incompatible ideals of communism and democracy rest upon opposed conceptions of nature, justice, and truth. Communism requires the subordination of individual rights to communal rights, secured by government; democracy acknowledges only individual rights, and sees in government only a means to implement individual rights. "Rights" are sanctioned powers; and differences concerning rights consequently involve conflicts concerning justice, morality, and truth. Differences of opinion concerning the nature of truth seem to be irreconcilable, because each of the two parties rejects the evidence and logic upon which the other party supports its argument. To reconcile philosophical differences, one must appeal to something that goes beyond philosophy. But what is there beyond philosophy?

Hegel, Croce, and many another thinker identify this struggle between individual and communal claims with human history itself. This struggle has given plot, direction,

and meaning to human life, they write. Certainly, it was
always necessary to write human history as political history,
or rather as political-economic history; and philosophical
thought has always been primarily a defense of individual
or communal human rights, supporting these upon a necessity said to be inherent in nature itself. But is there natural
justice? And if there is, is it communist or democratic
justice? *Is nature a community, or just a concourse of individuals?*

Out of this question, long familiar to man, proceeded an
inquiry into natural law, the fruits of which are natural
science and political theory. But the findings of science could
be diversely interpreted, so as to prove either that individual
things are cosmically conditioned, or that the cosmos is only
a sum of individual parts. There arose philosophy, seeking
to probe deeper. What sort of a world is it, the philosopher
asked, that makes science itself possible? Does the unity of
science not point to a community in universal nature? But
philosophers, too, divided into opposite camps. Some affirmed, others denied, that the unity of science indicates an
absolute necessity, binding knowledge because it binds the
world, or at least mankind, into unitary being. And this is
where we stand today! *Philosophy does not and cannot answer our most ultimate question!*

It must be admitted that in this long philosophical debate the advocates of cosmic necessity and universal community have had the best of it. The roster of great names includes ten able advocates of cosmic unity to one powerful
protagonist of radical plurality in nature. It is so patent
that the cosmos is cosmos, and not just chaos. The advocates
of unity have been able to call their view "rationalism,"
thereby identifying it with reason itself; and their opponents
have had to embrace skepticism, renouncing all intellectual
faith, in their desperate denial of the fact that the very pos-

sibility of science indicates a unity in nature, and a community in man, underlying and supporting every individual difference.

Yet, strangely enough, the day has not gone to the victors in this intellectual debate. It has gone to their skeptical opponents. More and more people have accepted skepticism, dooming man to everlasting ignorance, rather than renounce their belief in the absoluteness and ultimacy of individual being. The medieval mind was more skeptical than the mind of antiquity, in that it looked to a faith beyond reason. The modern mind was more skeptical than the medieval; and the contemporary mind is more skeptical than anything that has gone before. It would not be far from the truth to say that contemporary society is divided between those who support communism on rational grounds, and those who embrace skepticism as the price of democratic faith in the ultimacy of individual being.

But what is the verdict of science itself? To which of the two views does science more incline, in its rapid and far-flung development? This, of course, is the question which philosophy claims to answer, and it must not be begged. Yet it seems fair to say that science preserves a strange impartiality, dealing the cards to the opposed schools with equitable hand. In its fervent belief that the diversity of natural occurrence will be comprehended by some general hypothesis, the discovery of this hypothesis requiring only patience and ingenuity, science favors rationalism. But in its willingness to discard even the most imposing and elaborate system, if that system fails to do complete justice to particular fact, science supports the skeptic. The unity of nature never is, but always is to be, defined.

This incorruptible impartiality of science, which refuses to be umpire over the conflicting claims of philosophers, should give us pause. Is it possible that science still harbors a secret insight, which centuries of philosophical reflection upon science have failed to grasp? Is it possible that neither, or perhaps both, of the opposed contentions of philosophers may be valid? *Is there a truth lying beyond philosophy but within science?* Science is rationalistic in its pursuit of unitary theory, the success of which seems to indicate a unity in nature; yet it is skeptical in its refusal to accept any theory as final, exhaustive, definitive. Science seems to say that nature must, but never can, conform to unity and system. Of this oracular and cryptic saying, what philosopher has made sense?

Of this oracular and cryptic saying, no philosophy has yet made sense. There is evidently a reason beyond what we have called "reason," and a science beyond what we call "science." Nor is it difficult to see, today, where this more-than-science lies. The science of the past was theoretical science, satisfied to discover and to define the more constant structures of nature, such as physical and chemical structure. Theoretical science tells us that these structures exist; but it does not tell us why they exist, nor how they came to be, nor by what means they are maintained. Philosophy arose to ask these questions; but it has delivered no acceptable answer to them. The rationalistic philosopher assures us that nature is compelled by deep and inherent necessity to manifest unitary structure, and he tries to tell us what this universal necessity is. But the skeptic has little trouble in showing that a science which finds its criterion of reality and truth in *particular* fact really identifies necessity with particular necessity, not with universal necessity; and this would seem to be proof that nature is most ultimately plural, differentiated, particularized, individuated. The rationalist has constructed tremendous systems showing that particular character is "really" universal character, that difference is "really" identity, that plurality is "really" unity. The skeptic has pulled every system down. It is enough to set up a system, to have it bowled over.

The truth is that philosophy can ask, but not answer, that question. It can seek the ground and explanation of structure, into which a theoretical science, satisfied to discover structure, does not even inquire. It is no loss, perhaps, that philosophy should have spent twenty-five centuries in the vain effort to answer its own question. This long effort was needed in order to show that the question must be asked, and to make clear that neither theoretical science, nor any theoretical philosophy inquiring into the implications of that science, can hope to answer the question. *The question how the great structures of nature are established and maintained is not philosophical,* to be answered by an inquiry into the nature of knowledge. *It is scientific,* addressed to nature. But such inquiry is not theoretical science, seeking only to discover and to define structure. It is evolutionary science, inquiring into the creation of the world.

Understanding of the nature of the inquiry into the cause or ground of natural structures had to await the advent of evolutionary science. Evolutionary science is today with us; but there is still little understanding of the nature and scope of its inquiry, which is truly philosophical. Twenty-odd centuries of false philosophy have blinded us to the intent of the question, and confused us as to the locus of the answer to it. It must be seen that *philosophy was nothing but a bridge,* slowly and with difficulty built—for no man had yet crossed to the other side—*between the purely theoretical science of the past and the evolutionary science of the future.* Both philosophers and scientists—even would-be evolutionary scientists—looked ever more insistently to philosophy for an answer which only evolutionary science can give.

However, we can no longer remain in this blindness and ignorance. Philosophical error and intellectual impotence leave humanity divided, thrown into a conflict the issue of which can be only universal death. From this suicidal war of irreconcilable faiths we can be delivered only by a scientific truth which will undercut philosophical error, and reconcile faiths at present irreconcilable. The deliverance of evolutionary science is the deliverance of mankind, and of much more than man.

To this science, after a short preface, we will proceed.

* 2 *

THE NATURE AND
LOCUS OF TRUTH

WE must look to an empowered and expanded science, it was just said, for answers to questions which theoretical science does not ask, and which philosophy asks but cannot answer. This extension of scientific knowledge requires a delimitation of philosophical truth, opening to science a field of inquiry hitherto allocated to philosophy. We must learn where philosophy stops and whereunto science extends, if we will *no longer demand from philosophy what only science can give.*

Philosophical truth (or rational knowledge) is absolute and certain truth, self-evident, subject neither to proof nor to disproof. Scientific truth (or empirical knowledge) is dependent upon experience and is subject to confirmation or disproof by observed fact. It is reached by induction and hypothesis, and consequently it is never absolute and certain. At best only probable and approximate, it may be very highly probable, and very closely approximate.

It is desirable to extend the domain of rational knowledge as far as possible, because certain truth is preferable to probable truth. It is equally important to expand the domain of empirical knowledge, where belief can be supported upon observable evidence accessible to all men.

[8]

Most important, however, is to avoid the confusion of rational with empirical knowledge, because, once rational certainty is claimed for principles which are not rationally true, but which must and can be learned only empirically, questions which should be decided by the evidence of fact will be decided by brute force. It is consequently desirable to extend the domain of rational truth only to principles which find universal acceptance. Wherever opinions differ, let fact decide!

Philosophy therefore attempts to delimit reason, by discovering the minimum set of universal principles required to support empirical science. This would leave to empirical science every decision, except such decisions as must be made in order to begin scientific inquiry. It is clear that science proceeds otherwise than what is not science, so that it has its own presuppositions. Unfortunately, philosophy failed correctly to distinguish these basic rational truths from the scientific hypotheses supported upon them and reached by their means, so that its effort left confusion worse confounded. *Only in our own time have there come discoveries which at last make possible, after twenty-five centuries of philosophical failure, the accurate demarcation of rational truth from empirical hypothesis.*

Three discoveries make this demarcation possible.

(1) In the mid-nineteenth century, Darwin was able to establish the fact that animal and plant species have their temporal origins in individual variations. Today it is generally conceded that this evolutionary hypothesis is universal in scope. The whole of material creation, with all its specific structures, has evolved—as we say—in time. In other words, *no specific structure is eternal,* all specific structure is contingent and is subject to change.

(2) Early in the twentieth century, Einstein and other physicists showed that geometrical theory is empirical hy-

pothesis, and not rational knowledge, as had always been thought. This moved geometry out of the domain of absolute and certain truth, into the domain of empirical knowledge. *Geometry is physical hypothesis,* only probably and approximately true.

(3) Concurrently with this discovery came the proof by Russell and Whitehead, published in their epoch-making *Principia Mathematica,* that *arithmetic and logic are closely related disciples, flowing from a single set of axiomatic principles.* This demonstration transformed the study of logic and clarified the concept of arithmetical necessity.

The effect of the last two discoveries is to *draw a new and sharp line between rational truth and empirical science.* On the one side of this line lie arithmetic and logic; on the other side lie geometry, physics, chemistry, biology, and other natural and descriptive sciences. The effect of all three discoveries, taken together, is to require us to *distinguish* the *necessary order* of nature, which is that of arithmetical and logical necessity, from the *contingent* (or not necessary) *specific design* of nature, which is described by scientific hypothesis. There are, it is now clearly perceived, two very different sorts of patterns in nature (and not just one sort, as was earlier supposed). There is necessary order, and there is contingent design. This is why there is necessary or rational knowledge (arithmetical and logical theory) and probable empirical hypothesis (geometrical, physical, and other science).

The *order* of nature, engaged by arithmetic and logic, necessarily invests nature always and everywhere. This order is the warp on which is woven the woof of specific design, described by empirical science. Empirical science presupposes this necessary order, and consequently always makes use of arithmetic and logic. The order of nature is fixed, so that arithmetic and logic are certain, absolute, and necessary in their truth. But the *specific design* (or *structure*) of nature is contingent and in change, so that the empirical theory which describes structure is only probable and approximate.

Our task is to come to a better understanding of order and design, and of their relationship. The *order* of nature is the *necessary* plurality or *particularity* of nature. Nature is governed by an absolute necessity which requires it to be everywhere particularized, different, individuated. The constituents of nature, large and small, are all of necessity different, each identical with itself and identical with nothing else. However minutely we divide nature, its parts are different. Nature is everywhere what *particularly* was, is, will be. This is *particular necessity, the sole necessity known to us.* Whatever occurs is particularly necessitated, and must be just what it particularly is. It "could have been different" only if something had not occurred which did occur. This rational principle, which affirms particular necessity, is so obvious that it is hard to remember. Yet it is reason itself, active in every meaningful thought. Modern science differs from earlier science chiefly in the empirical rigor with which it applies this principle of particular necessity, which leads the scientist to quantitative method and mathematical formulation. *The sole identity in nature,* modern science insists, *is that of any particular with itself.*

It has never been clearly perceived that this empirical principle, which makes particular fact the sole criterion of truth, is also a rational principle. Yet, if nature is necessarily particularized and plural, if it is a plurality of distinct entities or particulars, it is necessarily countable and subject to arithmetical necessity. Arithmetical necessity, which is what keeps the counted entities distinct, never allowing them to merge with one another so that three be-comes four or two, is just the necessity which is particularity itself. *The necessity which generates rational knowledge, necessarily true, is particular necessity, not "universal necessity."* There is no "universal necessity," as Hume rightly saw. "Universal necessity" is just particular necessity misnamed. There is no "universal being," necessitating particulars to be what they are. All real being, and all real relationship, is particular. Reality is particular being, particularly necessitated to be what it particularly is. Things are really and necessarily different, through and through.

Arithmetic tells us how distinct entities may be grouped, numbered, combined, divided, recombined, all without violence to that necessity which requires the entities to re-main self-identical in every conceivable context. Since nature is constituted of distinct entities, or particulars, *arithmetic is a descriptive or natural science,* engaging the necessary order or particularity of nature. Arithmetic is at once the most abstract and the most concrete of sciences. It is most abstract in that it engages only the particularity which differentiates nature, in complete abstraction from the contingent specific design of nature. It is most concrete in that it describes the plurality of particulars which constitute material nature itself, and which carry all specific design. Arithmetic is the science of necessity, and therefore of possibility. What is possible is what necessity allows. Five can be two and three, or four and one; it cannot be three and three. Arithmetic describes any conceivable world, plural and particularized, with or without specific design. It describes even a chaos of particulars, void of all design.

Logic moves one step toward actuality. It contemplates a reality at once particularized and specified. It does not engage the reality actually specified as is our world, however. It contemplates a reality specified only as A, B, C, etc. It is still a science of the possible, descriptive of *any* particularized and specified world. But since this world of ours is in fact specifically structured, *logic describes our world* along with other possible worlds. Arithmetic and logic hold of heaven and hell, as well as of this world of ours, which apparently lies somewhere between. As the theologian knew, even God, if he is intelligent, must defer to logic.

Logical necessity is still just arithmetical necessity, which is particular necessity. Logic requires that, if *all* the particulars specified as A are further specified as B, then at least *some* particulars specified as B are necessarily also specified as A. It tells us that if no particulars of the type A are of the type B, then no particulars of the type B can possibly be of the type A. These conclusions are required by particular necessity, which requires each particular to be identically specified, in every context of thought. Logic allows us to think of the identical particular twice, in different contexts.

The above inferences illustrate *deductive logic*. They show that deductive necessity is the same necessity as that which requires two always to be one and one, never more and never less. A particular can cease to exist; but if it existed, it can never be truly held not to have existed. Donald C. Williams has shown in his short treatise *The Ground of Induction* that inductive logic also rests upon this same arithmetical necessity.

Inductive logic, Williams shows, requires us to hold that the observed sample of any sort of thing is probably and approximately a good sample. For example, if 50 per cent of the rabbits we have *observed* are male, we are compelled by logical necessity to conclude that *probably* 50 per cent, *approximately,* of *all* rabbits are male. This inductive inference is necessitated simply by the plurality or particularity of the world. If there are specified pluralities, i.e. discernible classes of particulars, then any selection or sample of a class is of necessity (approximately and probably) a good sample. We should not allow ourselves to be duped or confused, as was earlier thought, by the fact that a necessary inference may lead only to a probable conclusion. It is the conclusion, not the inference, which is probable. The inference is necessary and, as such, certain! If you choose one marble from a bag which contains twice as many white as black marbles, you are rationally compelled to conclude that the probability of drawing a white marble is two out of three, or two-thirds. This is the same necessity as that which requires you to say that, if all of the marbles in the bag are white, the marble drawn will necessarily and certainly be white. Induction is just one sort of deduction.

The foregoing paragraph informs us that, and why, all empirical knowledge is probable and approximate, not certain and absolute. It is because it is reached by inductive reasoning, from samples of the world. Empirical science presupposes the rational knowledge which is arithmetic and logic. It could not move a step without this science of the necessary and possible. But science goes further, to discover approximately and probably what is the actual specificity or structure of this world. It supports its discovery of the actual upon its absolute and certain knowledge of what is necessary and possible in any particularized and specified world.

What, we may ask, do we mean by *specificity,* specific character, structure, design? We saw that the order of nature is the necessary particularity of the real, the identity of the particular only with itself, the difference of the particular from all else. Particulars are necessarily different; but they may very well be similar. Things must be different, even to be similar. Identical twins must be different twins—they cannot be one and the same identical twin, because they are two and not one. But *things do not have to be similar, in order to be different.* This is why particularity is necessary, but specific character contingent or not necessary. Specific character is any widespread, enduring, and objective similarity among particulars. A species, or type, or real class, is a plurality of particulars all particularly different, yet all specifically similar, i.e. similar in a similar way. This A resembles that B, and the B resembles a C, and the C resembles a D, and so on; and the similarity between A and B resembles the similarity between B and C, C and D, etc. This is what we mean by a real class, any two members of which are similar in much the same way. No two members are identical in any way. If they were identical in any way, they would be identical in every way, and be not two but one. Discernibles are nowise identical. *No quality of a thing can be literally identical with the quality of another thing.* Qualities can be as similar as you please, short of being identical. Particularity or difference is real, absolute, inexpugnable, ubiquitous. *This is the principle of reason, upon which all science and all sanity depend. All philosophical and intellectual confusion is due to departure from this principle of reason, which affirms the non-identity of discernibles.*

All knowledge whatsoever comes from perception. Whence else could it come? We immediately perceive both particular character and similarity—for example, we see our five fingers. The fingers are all different, yet all similar. These perceived differences and similarities, however, are fleeting, and subjectively conditioned by our own nature; and we move from them, by induction and hypothesis, to a knowledge of enduring, widely spread, objective similarities, i.e. to specific types. By means of this knowledge of specific type, which, be it observed, is *always* reached and only to be reached by inductive inference, we come to a knowledge of real and objective particularity. For example, we may infer the existence of an invisible particular atom or electron from our perception of its visible track.

Thus all knowledge of reality, all that is not just sensed as an animal senses it, is reached through knowledge of specific type. What we perceive is the clue to what we discover. Our sensations are real, but they are not knowledge. It is often argued that, because specific type is known only by inference, it is not real. This, we see, reverses the truth. It is because it is known by inference that it may be real. *What we cannot validly infer, we call "unreal."* You do not call a flying pink elephant "real," even though you see it. This is common sense: to know that the real is known only by inference.

All knowledge whatsoever, even arithmetic and logic, is obtained from experience. The difference between rational and empirical knowledge is not, therefore, that the latter does and the former does not derive from experience. The difference is that rational knowledge, however derived, cannot be upset by further experience, whereas empirical knowledge can. It is reason that assures us both of the necessary particularity of nature, and of the contingent status of specific character. Those truths could never be learned from experience alone, without reasoning.

We have now clearly demarcated the respective spheres of rational and empirical knowledge, which is to say the respective spheres of philosophy and science. *Philosophy is rational knowledge of particular necessity; and it includes only arithmetic and logic,* which engage the order of particular necessity. Everything else that can be known must be learned empirically, and is knowledge of contingent specific character. This disposes of all past and present philosophy, which lies somewhere between, or above, or below logic and science. There is only arithmetic, logic, and empirical science, all of which rest on rational insight into particular necessity. This insight mightily extends the domain allocated to science. Everything that has been called "philosophy" has been pseudoscience, pretending to be rational and certain knowledge of what can be known only empirically and probably. Our purpose is to explore and if possible annex this new domain, opened to scientific inquiry by the three epochal discoveries earlier mentioned.

Before we do this, let us cast a glance at the philosophical errors we are leaving behind us, both in gratitude for their approach to the truth, and in order not to be deluded by intellectual piety into taking them along with us. We can afford to bless our intellectual progenitors only when we have written their epitaphs. The child must be weaned to live. Let the child live! God, let there be life!

The truths just presented are really those of common sense, which departs from them only through intellectual and verbal confusion. If they are not altogether easy to state, and require a little special terminology, this is because they are so obvious and familiar that common sense rarely needs to utter them. No man of common sense would ever think of his children as literally identical in any respect. Their noses might be most similar; but after all, they are on different faces; and there are two noses, not one. Further, these truths have been highly developed and consistently applied by modern science, ever since Roger Bacon in the thirteenth century inaugurated modern science, by requiring that knowledge shall exactly conform both to arithmetical necessity, and to particular necessity as this is revealed in observed particular fact.

Why, then, did it take philosophy twenty-five centuries to grasp and to state clearly these implicit assumptions of common sense and science? Why did the truth have to be forced upon philosophy by science and logic? The reason is that philosophy was asking a question which neither it, nor common sense, nor the science of the past was able to answer. The science of the past was a purely theoretical science, discovering and defining in its theories the specific structures of nature, but not inquiring into the origin of these structures. The philosopher legitimately desired to know why these structures exist. Science and common sense only reiterated that they do exist—there just are these species and specific structures. But the philosopher demanded a reason, a cause, an origin. We can see today, and since Darwin we ought to be able to believe, that the species and structures of nature originate in individual variations, i.e. in particular necessity. But this seemed both incredible and unintelligible. So the philosopher sought some "universal ground" of similarity and specificity of type.

Greek and medieval philosophy looked to "universal necessity," something over and above particular necessity, to explain why particulars are specifically similar; and they taught that "universal necessity" is broken up by particular differences into "specific necessities." There is "universal causation," said Plato, the profoundest of these earlier thinkers; and this "formal causation" always works to persuade the particularly necessitated items of nature into specific forms. But modern science, as we noted, has identified "formal" or "universal" necessity, for example as it appears in arithmetical necessity, with *particular* necessity.

Modern philosophers, in their effort to explain modern science, broke into hostile camps. Philosophical realists argued that since theoretical science is possible only if nature is specifically structured, and theoretical science actually exists, nature *must* be structured; and to say that nature *must* be structured seems to imply that structure is universally necessitated. It is true that nature must be structured *if* knowledge is to exist. There could not be knowledge of nature if there were no structure. But the question is whether structure *necessarily* exists, not whether it does exist. Today, we have to entertain the possibility that man may annihilate life. The annihilation of life would erase from nature all social, psychological, and biological structure, so that social, psychological, and biological theories would describe nothing; but, if these structures may conceivably disappear, so may all specific structure, leaving a chaotic or formless world. This chaos would still be particularly ordered, but it would lack all specific design. Specific character is possible and actual; but it is contingent and not necessary. There is no "specific necessity."

However, this sort of rebuttal carried little weight so long as the relations between arithmetic, logic, and other science were not understood. The necessity defined by arithmetic and logic was mistakenly attributed to specific form, or type, in the notions of "geometrical necessity," "physical necessity," etc. Yet it was also apparent to many thinkers that such "specific necessity" is both incompatible with moral responsibility, and unthinkable if empirical science is right in making observed particulars the test of general theory. Consequently there arose the skeptical philosophy which, in order to discredit the fallacies of "specific necessity" and "universal necessity," rejected all necessity and causation whatsoever, including particular necessity—thus throwing out the baby with the bath water.

David Hume, the father of modern skepticism, argued that causal necessity is no necessity, but only an observed similarity of sequence among particular occurrences. If

A is often enough followed by B, he said, we come to expect B after A, and to attribute to A some power to necessitate B; yet, however closely we look, we cannot discover in any particular event this alleged power to determine its successor. We find *that* A always or usually precedes B, but not *why*. We therefore cannot say that A must precede B, or that B must follow A. We can say only that A will probably be followed by B, and B probably preceded by A. We are mentally constrained to *expect* B after A; but nature is not in any way necessitated to *produce* B after A. We find no necessity in nature. If we find it anywhere, we find it in ourselves, in our habitual expectancies; but these habits can be and often are broken, and replaced by better habits, bringing expectancy closer to fact.

Hume's description is psychologically true. It is also philosophically correct in its discovery of the true status of general knowledge as probable or less than certain, and in its affirmation of the non-necessity, or contingency, of specific type. Hume's frontal attack upon the fallacy of "universal causation" made him the great champion of empirical science, and the most influential and conse- quential philosopher of modern times. It is all the more necessary to distinguish what was sound in his analysis from what was erroneous and misleading; for this error leads us back into that fallacy of "universal necessity" which it was Hume's honest intention and effective achievement to in- dict.

Hume's error sprang from his elliptical or shorthand manner of statement. He says that we observe A to be fol- lowed by B, and conclude that A necessitates B. This is not strictly true. We observe particulars *a, b, c* . . . of the type A, respectively followed by particulars *d, e, f* . . . of the type B; and we conclude by inductive necessity (and not by habit, for the habit has to be formed and cultivated) that any particular of the type A will be followed by some particular of the type B. In other words, we observe not A followed by B, but the particular *a* followed by the particular *d*, the particular *b* followed by the particular *e* etc. We note the *similarity of the particular sequences ad, be, cf* . . . , and we call such similarity "causal similarity." Of course, all knowledge of causal similarity is knowledge of specific and contingent fact, and therefore probable only. There is no universal necessity compelling nature to present or to produce similarities of sequence, or any simple or complex similarities. But there is a particular necessity which compels nature to be always and everywhere, *in its relationships as well as in what is related,* just what it particularly is. At least this is the affirmation of reason, without which no knowledge, no thought, and no intelligible statement whatsoever are possible.

If there are relations of any sort between earlier and later particular occurrence—and there indubitably are, because we have partial knowledge of them, supporting probable prediction—these relations are *particularly* necessitated to be just what they are. It is the similarity among particular necessitations that is noted as causal connection. But if we have observed particulars of the type A to be followed by particulars of the type B, we are compelled by inductive logical necessity to infer that all particulars of the type A are probably followed by particulars approximately of the type B. In other words, we are learning something of the specific and contingent structure of nature, which is quite real, although only probably and approximately knowable.

Hume himself, it follows, had to assume particular causal necessity in his analysis of causal knowledge, which was really an introspective pseudopsychology. He assumed that a particular perception *necessitates* the recall of earlier perceptions similar to it, that this earlier perception *necessarily* brings with it something of its context, and that this combination of perception and memory *necessitates* our anticipation of a similar context. For example, he assumed that, if we see Brown, we are necessitated to recall Brown's dog which always accompanied him, and again necessitated to expect to find the dog near by. These recalls and anticipations occur involuntarily and by natural necessity. What Hume actually denied was the necessity of specific similarity in the external world, on the ground that all such necessity is the projection into external nature of a real, specifically psychological necessity in ourselves.

This unfortunate Humian "psychologism," mistaking psychology for logic, has remained with us, to defeat philosophy and to infect the intellect itself, until today it is so widespread and deep-seated that it amounts to a universal skepticism threatening all intellectual faith and destroying civilization. In truth, there is no more psychological necessity than there is physical, geometric, or other "specific necessity." Whatever we know or learn of psychological process is reached by means of empirical hypothesis, supported upon arithmetic and deductive and inductive logic, rational sciences which affirm absolute and real particular necessity, and the contingency of all specific type. The Humian "psychologism" propagates an epistemological mysticism, the devotees of which profess devotion to science even while they look to a mystical, inward-turned intuition informing them of ultimate things. Suppose that they do have this inner intuition! Is it not only by induction and causal inference that its deliverance can be held true, of and by other minds than their own?

Contemporary philosophical literature is still largely a perpetuation of the philosophical errors of the past. Self-styled "empiricists" will, at one and the same time, enunciate complicated "verification theories of meaning," yet reject the principle of particular causal necessity needed to make these theories intelligible. They tell us that the truth and even the meaning of a statement are "determined" by the particular occurrences which verify predictions based upon the statement, i.e. by something in the future. It is true that particular predictions are verified by future occurrences; but what the verified prediction confirms is the *general hypothesis* used in the prediction. How should we ever make a prediction, or confirm a theory, if the *meaning* of the prediction and the theory appeared only at the time of the verifying occurrence? And how should we make any prediction, or accept any occurrence as verifying a prediction, or accept any verification of prediction as confirming a hypothesis, if we did not know that earlier particular occurrences, now known to us, causally necessitate those occurrences yet to be which will verify or fail to verify our prediction. The verification theory of meaning is simply an attempt to side-track the process of induction, to dispense with inductive logic, and to demand from empirical knowledge a certainty which no inductive knowledge can possibly have. It is a confusion of meaning with truth and of ideas with external actualities.

It would take a volume, or rather a library, to nail to the door all of the contemporary fallacies which perpetuate past philosophical error by the denial, implicit or overt, or by the simultaneous denial and affirmation, of the principle of particular necessity. There is little value in scotching these fallacies one by one. An elucidation which only perpetuates polemics is unprofitable. However, it may be said that the philosophical "realist" will always be found at some point to confuse real identity, which is that of any particular with itself, with some real similarity grounded in difference. The "realist" argues that similarity can only be "grounded in identity"—that similar qualities, for example, are different "manifestations" of an identical quality. Since all quality, like everything that is, is particularized, this is only an insistent confusion of difference with sameness. *Because* everything is necessarily different, everything is necessarily similar, says this "realist." He confuses the necessary difference of things with their universal but contingent similarity. And so he confuses arithmetic and logic with empirical theory.

The philosophical "realist" is truly a sort of naïf or uncritical idealist. Following Hume came philosophers who took seriously his fallacious reasoning that all necessity is a psychological or mental necessity, projected by the mind into nature. In this case, they argued, what we call "nature" or "reality" is truly something that is determined by mind or thought or experience. Psychological necessity is identical with "universal necessity," and nature is truly mind. Common sense at once asks the idealist whether psychological necessity moved the sun through space before man was, or mind was, or thought was. The idealist no longer turns upon this common sense the pained look of an orthodox parent whose child has questioned the immaculate conception. He turns to a complicated epistemology which confuses the determination of events by events with the "determination" or ascertainment of events by the scientist. The determination of events by events is by particular necessity; but the scientific "determination" of events involves the assumption of universal structure, because events cannot be described in specific terms if there is no specific structure enabling description. Thus, by an easy equivocation and verbal duplicity, the idealist confounds common sense, or at least silences its objections, by identifying particular necessity with a specific universal necessity which does not and cannot exist. This equivocation appears in a thousand variations, and is the favorite device of pragmatists, "philosophers of science," and others who are usually unaware of their idealistic presuppositions.

Empirical realism, as we may call the clear distinction of the necessary order engaged by arithmetic and logic from the contingent and specific design which is known by induction and hypothesis, emancipates us from these errors of the philosophical "realist." But it does not answer, it only puts more clearly and insistently, the question which past philosophy either falsely answered or skeptically evaded. If there is only particular necessity, and no universal nor specific necessity, why is there structure and specific character in nature? This question might be phrased: What brought the world out of chaos, what maintains species, structure, cosmic design? Why do things remain specifically similar, if the sole necessity in the world is that which keeps them particular and different? The honest and courageous answer to this question is: We do not know; but we have every reason to believe we can learn.

Clearly, if only particular necessity exists, species and structures are generated, maintained, and on occasion destroyed by particular necessity. The cosmos is somehow the creature of its own particular constituents. But is this credible, is it conceivable? How can it be understood?

Darwin helped to make it credible, conceivable, and intelligible when he showed that animal and plant species have their origin and maintenance in individually variant organisms. We must clarify and amplify this Darwinian insight, which reminds us that each living generation is the creature of the last and the creator of the next. We must extend Darwin's insight to nature at large, so that we come to understand how all structure, or that which bears it, is continually regenerated. Atoms and molecules of themselves maintain their specific similarities, which originated in time.

Darwin's great evolutionary hypothesis was vitiated by residual metaphysical and philosophical errors. His hypothesis stated that species are the result of "natural selection," exerted by the "environment" which works upon individual variations. What is this "natural selection" that has shaped inorganic matter into the many specific forms of plant and animal life? What is this "environment" that has determined all specific structure, producing cosmos out of chaos? Is this environment empty space, which first produced and then molded into specific form all material being? What are "natural selection" and "the environment" but new words for the "universal and eternal necessity" of the Greek philosopher, or the eternal and omnipotent God of the theologian?

We must pursue an evolutionary science emancipated from these pious fallacies. But it is evident that in our scientific pursuit of that creative power, which these fallacies glozed over and hid, we shall need new concepts and new ways of thought, different from and going beyond those of a merely theoretical science, philosophy, and theology. No man has really, knowing what he was doing, yet dared to inquire into the creation of the world. We can expect the inquiry to reach unprecedented and astonishing conclusions, justifying the statement that there are things in heaven and earth undreamt of in philosophy, and requiring us to credit what is as yet incredible. The inquiry will certainly not be easy, and it will hardly be safe. It cannot hope for the good will of those who desire only to see phrased in new and intriguing terms what already is universally known, familiar, orthodox. Let those whose aim is social reputation and apparent success (which today includes scholarly reputation and academic success) lay this book aside! It took a certain impiety in Hume to consign all that is not arithmetic and empirical hypothesis—all theology and metaphysics—to the flames. But what is here proposed is somewhat more defiant. It is here proposed to rescue from the flames of skepticism, and to restore to empirical science and common sense, those terrible and "blasphemous" truths which science and common sense have been only too willing to let philosophy and theology decently enshroud and safely inter. Plato made Socrates say that men after their death shall learn astonishing things. But I now tell you that men shall know these things, revealing the secrets of creation and putting into their hands the levers of destiny, while they yet live!

* 3 *

THE KEY LIES IN BIOLOGY

WHEN Darwin established the fact that species originate in individual variations, he overturned, almost singlehanded and overnight, what had been philosophy. Theoretical science knows the individual only as a member of some existing class. Theoretical philosophy, reflecting upon theoretical science, necessarily failed to elucidate what it is that relates an individual to its class. *But evolutionary science clarifies that relationship. It makes the individual the progenitor and preserver of its class.* Reflection upon evolutionary science must deliver itself of something very different from the philosophy which knew only theoretical science.

The agelong limitation of the intellect to theoretical knowledge calls for explanation. There were ancient Greeks—for example, Anaximander and Empedocles—who put forward very explicit accounts of natural evolution. Why were these evolutionary hypotheses buried and forgotten, much as was Aristarchus' discovery of the earth's revolution about the sun, rediscovered by Copernicus sixteen centuries later? Greek philosophy, wedded to eternal species, silenced the blasphemy of prophets who taught the evolution of species in time. But what was its motive in so doing?

The motive was political. The Greek philosopher wished

to establish the sanctity of the political community or state. He taught that the specific distinction of man, a "political animal," is that he inhabits a state and conforms in his behavior to public law. This identification of the state with the specific human form argued the eternity and absolute justice of the state—but only if "species" are eternal. So the philosopher taught that an eternal, absolute, and universal necessity manifests itself in eternal species; and in man this universal necessity specifically requires conformity to state law. Few Greeks could believe that law and the state are man-made; and those who did could be ruled out of order.

But modern society arose to advance the faith that society makes its own law, and creates the state. Society was compelled to advance still further, and to say that in a society continuously remaking its law by progressive legislation the individuals comprising society are the creators of the state and of its law. If man is a political animal, the human "species" is evidently in evolution. Toward the end of the eighteenth century, certain thinkers used the word "progress" to indicate the fact of human evolution; and, a half-century later, Darwin was able to announce that all "species" originate and evolve as the result of individual differences.

Unfortunately, this evolutionary hypothesis, probably because it had to combat theological prejudice, at once became identified with certain subsidiary hypotheses which either make it unintelligible, or distort it into an altogether immoral doctrine. Even Darwin portrayed evolution as a continual struggle for survival, the weaker going to the wall so that the strong might perpetuate their kind. Darwin was influenced by Malthus, who propagated the horrible doctrine that human populations must *of necessity* multiply beyond their means of subsistence, malnutrition taking off the weaker. Darwin made cardinal use of this doctrine in his concept of a natural selection which destroys, before they come to maturity, the worse adapted members of every living species. The better adaptations, those which preserve or improve a species, were attributed to chance variations. The worse adaptations were also attributed to chance; but in their case a destroying angel stood by, ready to cut them off. The sole and sufficient agents of evolution, according to this Darwinian formula, are chance and death. The individual organism has a completely passive role. It really matters nothing whether the organism struggles or not. If it is born adapted, it survives; if unadapted, it perishes. What is well adapted here may be ill adapted there. Even if the organism be well adapted and have progeny, what effects evolution is only its heritable character, about which it can do nothing. We must conclude either that man does not evolve as animals evolve, or that his effort to make progress is of no evolutionary consequence, and rests upon a pitiful illusion.

But the notion of natural selection exerted by the environment ceases under examination to be intelligible; and not a few biologists today assure their students that the whole idea of evolution is a fallacy or pseudoconcept. We can find no evidence of evolutionary progress, they say, nor of any effective natural selection. We observe that some species persist, some multiply into new species, and some become extinct; but we find no explanation for these different destinies. Further, if we say that the whole evolution of life, from protoplasm to man, was brought about by environmental selection, must we not suppose either that all existent and extinct species somehow existed "potentially" in the first protoplasm, or that there was in the physical environment a preformed pattern, waiting to shape protoplasm by "selection" into all the species that have been? Or shall we conceive evolution itself to proceed initially in the environment, this environmental evolution then being repeated or reflected in the organic evolution which is its effect? But how can we suppose a lifeless and uniform environment to determine the evolution of the myriad species composing the organic economy? Is "the environment" very God, creating a living world to his heart's desire? Then why all the blood and tears?

The Darwinian doctrine of evolution successfully established the *fact* of the temporal origin of species; but it aggravated eighteenth century skepticism, already dubious of natural causation as the result of philosophical criticism, by attributing the course of organic evolution to "chance"; and it added to this intellectual doubt a new moral skepticism, by portraying nature as essentially a brutish struggle for individual survival. By the twentieth century, skepticism had become so deep and wide as to leave no room for scientific and moral faith. The present century pursues science not for knowledge but for use. An experimental science proposes to control nature without understanding nature. Do this and you will get that, no man knows why! Nor should you ask, adds the pragmatist.

Fortunately, the twentieth century also advanced scientific and logical discoveries removing the grounds of philosophical skepticism; and it further developed *new biological disciplines which correct, clarify, and expand the Darwinian hypothesis.* The nineteenth century conceived of evolution metaphorically, as the impulsion of a stream of organisms against a sort of environmental grid, the better adapted organisms passing through the grid to reproduce their kind, the worse adapted failing to pass through and perishing with their seed. This metaphor covered a failure of causal analysis. The adapted survive, or "are selected." What is not "selected" is not adapted.

The fit survive, but "the fit" are, by definition, those which do survive. "Adaptation" and "selection" are just two words for one and the same fact, that of persistence. They are not cause and effect, they explain nothing. The notion of a causal interaction between the species and the environment, in "the selection of the well adapted" or the "survival of the fit," was simply the observable fact that some and not all organisms survive to maturity, that only some types persist. For the individual variations, held to determine what survives or perishes, were attributed to chance! The appearance of causal explanation was a verbal illusion. The doctrine really attributed all evolutionary change to chance, i.e. to unknown causes.

But with the twentieth century came the development of *genetic science,* which makes possible the causal explanation of evolutionary change. Individual variations are not due to chance, but conform to "laws of inheritance" which are increasingly well understood. Each species has its distinctive heritable genic type, transmitted from generation to generation. Each genic type occurs in several isotypes called "allelotypes." Each organism has its set of genes, typical for its species; but no two organisms have genes of quite the same allelic forms. Where reproduction is bisexual, there is a reshuffling in each generation of the allelic sets, no organism of the daughter generation having exactly the same allelotype as any organism of the parent generation. The geneticist is able to follow this varied inheritance through successive generations.

The science of genetics revolutionizes evolutionary inquiry. It is as if the species were a deck of cards constantly gathered up and redealt according to a fixed procedure. Individual variations occur within determinable limits, and the probability of the incidence of any heritable type becomes calculable. Given sufficient knowledge of genic structure, and of the sorts of development determined by variable genotype, the geneticist can predict the probable course of evolutionary change.

The science of genetics does not yet, however, explain the origin of new species, possessed of new genic type. It was thought for a while that the occurrence of mutations, i.e. of radical modifications undergone by individual genes, perhaps as the result of chemical change, might explain the emergence of new species, i.e. of new genic type. However, mutations are known to occur in considerable quantity in all species, and to be distributed in successive generations through a population without inducing specific change. Mutations, just because they would explain everything, explain nothing. Mutations are probably only striking instances of the particular variation which must continually characterize all genes and alleles. It is the genic or allelic type, not the individual gene nor the allele, that is fixed and invariable. The individual organism will always vary slightly in its individual genes, and it may vary importantly and discoverably in its allelotype. It is observable that the adult organisms of a species vary in size, weight, and other properties. It is known that their character is genically determined. There is every reason to believe that genes and alleles also vary within their type, individually.

As a matter of fact, the geneticist finds many sorts of genic change which might, under certain circumstances, lead to speciation, i.e. to change of adaptive type originating a new species; but, to discover how any sort of speciation has in fact come about, he must leave the laboratory and proceed to observe natural populations, where the origin of new species actually takes place. Here he finds himself in need of a new concept, that of the *breeding population*.

The concept of the breeding population (for the sake of brevity we will usually write "population" or "group") *replaces the earlier concept of the species.* The species usually meant the whole class of similar organisms which *could* or *might,* under appropriate circumstances, productively interbreed. *The breeding population is the group of individuals which actually do interbreed.* This group is not so easily demarcated as the species; but the species concept also breaks down—for example, where different species interbreed to produce hybrids, and in sympatric species which do not interbreed when they specifically "should." The concept of the breeding population is not so neat as the concept of the species. It is relative to time, in that the group of organisms which interbreed within a single season will not be identical with the group of organisms interbreeding within several generations, nor with the breeding population considered over a period of years or centuries. But the neatness of the species concept was deceptive, because the species is usually a number of populations, descended presumably from a single earlier population, but no longer genetically associated. This means that *the species as such is not the unit of evolutionary change.* The species, indeed, is really a subgenus, and not a real unit of any kind. It is populations, not species, that emerge, undergo "specific" change, and persist or become extinct. It might be said that when a single breeding population divides into two such populations, the members of one group no longer breeding with members of the other, either or both of these two populations may originate a new "species"; but this is not the way the word "species" is commonly used, although it does indicate the way in which all organic types have originated.

The population is that group of organisms so particularly related that they are *necessitated* to interbreed, and consequently do interbreed, to produce progeny. If a population is by any cause divided into two inbreeding but not interbreeding groups, there are now two *de facto* populations and not one. The division and consequent multiplication of populations is the condition of speciation, or the rise of new specific types. If, as seems likely, all terrestrial life had a common origin, then a single population has been divided again and again, to form all of the populations, varieties, species, genera, families, and higher categories of life that have existed on earth since life began.

There are, accordingly, two sorts of real and effective units in living matter, and not one only. *The organism is a real and natural unit,* in that life persists only in unitary and living organisms. But *the breeding population also is a real and natural unit,* in that life persists only in unitary self-regenerating groups. The individual organism does not independently reproduce its kind, as a rule. The organism does not evolve. It is the population, not the individual and not the species, that evolves. To return to the unfortunate metaphor of the environmental grid, it is populations, not individuals merely, that must pass through the grid if life is to persist. There is a good deal of evidence showing that populations become extinct if they decrease beyond a certain point, and that the populations which have continually replenished the earth have been sizable groups.

This concept of the population or self-regenerative group promises to become the most important concept of biological science, and, indeed, of all natural science. It is the idea we have waited for so long, in order to state properly, and so to solve, the problems which philosophy improperly stated and failed to solve. It is fortunate that we should establish this important concept today, when another concept, that of atomic energy released by the disintegration of atoms, promises either tremendously to empower man or altogether to destroy him. The concept of the group must provide the power required to keep the concept of atomic energy from blowing mankind to pieces. We should not belittle concepts as only "ideas." The concept of atomic energy is an instrument capable of exploding this earth. The concept of the population or group has an equal, but constructive, power. It turns biological science inside out, like a glove, reorienting our whole conception of living process. The population concept carries us from the bacteria to the animals, and from animal life to human society, making the sciences of biology and sociology continuous, reciprocally instructive, one. It makes organic evolution intelligible and explicable, as will presently be seen. Let us clarify our conception of the group, with its persistence or change of type. Type is always adaptive type, a sort of adaptation. The *group* is the plurality of organisms so *associated,* i.e. *reciprocally adapted,* that they effect *gene exchange,* which is usually the condition of reproduction and always a condition of group persistence. Let us designate this association (group adaptation, reproductive adaptation) as R adaptation. It is more important as a condition of the persistence of group and type than *external adaptation,* which we will designate as E adaptation. This latter is *biotic* (to organisms of other groups), or *physical* (to the local and temporal habitat). All group *persistence,* and with this all persistence and change of adaptive type, *depends upon the variable relationship between group adaptation and external adaptation.*

Let us give to the individual gene-complex which results from genic mixis (gene exchange between two individuals) the designation *genic constitution;* and let us call *genic structure* the pattern of genic constitutions in any associated group. (The geneticist sometimes speaks of the "gene-pool," meaning this structure as it is transmitted through the successive generations of a group.) Although genes are real and particular, there is genic type, knowledge of which is reached by inference from uniformities of adaptive development, conditioned by uniformities of genic type. Genes of the same type may show variety, designated as allelic type. The pattern of allelic type varies in different individuals; and allelic type is reshuffled in each reproduction of type effected by gene exchange. The geneticist can trace the descent of "allelotype" through successive generations, and calculate how quickly it might spread through a group as the result of periodic gene exchange. We are concerned, fortunately, only with the largest features of this complicated business of genetic inheritance.

There is reason to believe that different genes, or sets of genes, condition different adaptive developments. R genes condition reproductive development, and different sets of E genes condition various developments of externally adaptive character. Thus, a given genic constitution may contain R genes, conditioning good reproductive development, together with E genes conditioning good externally adaptive development in one respect, poor in a second respect, average in a third respect, and so on. Periodic gene exchange constantly reshuffles the heritable type, so that good reproductive development goes now with one pattern of externally adaptive development and now with another pattern. By and large, as the generations pass, there is continual elimination of genic type conditioning poor adaptive development of any sort. The individuals carrying such type either do not mature or, on maturing, they produce few progeny. The sterile individual does not reproduce its type, i.e. produce progeny closely similar to itself in genic content and consequent development. This elimination of poor genic type, with consequent increase in proportion of better genic type, we may call "selection." Even with fixed environmental conditions, there may be considerable selection of genic type and consequent change of genic structure in a group. New sorts of genic constitution, conditioning new sorts of adaptive development, constantly arise; and it is accordingly less the change of specific type, and more its remarkable constancy, that calls for explanation. Our interest, however, is less in the persistence of species than in the evolution of species, and in the persistence of specific, generic, and wider type. We wish to know why some species are extinct; why some seem to be fixated; how species originated; and why some groups evidently were adaptable, to become the progenitors of large species, and even of the orders, classes, and great phyla of life.

We distinguished R genes from E genes. Let us further distinguish Rg from Rp genes, respectively conditioning good and poor reproductive development; and similarly, let Eg and Ep genes designate genes which respectively determine good and poor externally adaptive development.

There is constant "selection" of genic constitutions of the well adapted type RgEg. As a consequence of periodic gene exchange, constitutions of all possible types (RgEg, RgEp, RpEg, and RpEp) must continually occur; but the last of the four types, RpEp, poorly adapted both ways, will scarcely become established, individuals of this unfortunate type commonly failing to reproduce their type. The intermediate types may precariously persist; but the type RgEg will be securely established, and will increasingly dominate the group, with other types being progressively eliminated. Thus, *every group should show adaptive progress,* becoming better reproductively adapted and more fertile, and also better adapted externally. All groups should be of the RgEg type. Why, if this be so, is there extinction of species, fixation of species, and evolution of new genera, orders, and classes of species?

For two reasons. First, the very increase of life, due to

the continual selection of good adaptive type, changes external conditions, both for the population that enjoys increase and for its neighboring populations. Secondly, not all populations are adaptable, most of the types we call "species" being relatively fixated, and persisting in dependence upon environmental stability. The evolution of life presupposes, however, the past existence of highly adaptable populations, ancestral to the existing classes, orders, families, and genera of species. The problem, therefore, is to discover what keeps or makes groups adaptable, and what makes and leaves them fixated, dependent for persistence on factors external to themselves.

Prior to the rise of genetic analysis, the evolutionary scientist paid little attention to factors internal to the group, in his attempt to explain evolutionary change. The whole emphasis was placed upon external adaptation, with the assumption of close correlation between persistence or change of adaptive type and persistence or change of environmental conditions. Today, it is difficult to understand this long neglect of reproductive adaptation, determining relative fertility. Obviously, the more fertile individuals have a disproportionately large influence in determining what sorts of adaptive types, both reproductive and external, will be established in a group. If reproductive character is adaptive character—and it evidently is so, some pairings of organisms and genic mixes being more fertile than others—a process of reproductive or group selection is always going on within each associated group. Moreover, this sort of selection conditions the other sort, because it presents to the environment the material from which some parts may then be "externally selected." The sterile individual or pair, however well adapted externally, is of little or no consequence in persistence or change of type, because its type is just not reproduced. Poor externally adaptive type, on the other hand, may precariously persist, if it is conjoined with high fertility. *The major progress, underlying and supporting all evolution of external adaptive type, has been that of reproductive adaptation and fertility.*

Once this fact is clearly seen and fully appreciated, it becomes evident that *good reproductive adaptation is also responsible for adaptability*—something quite other than adaptedness—*to external change.* (Perhaps the ambiguity of the word "adaptation" confused thought. The word is used either for the process which adapts this to that, or for the product which issues from the process. "That is a good adaptation," we say, speaking of a highly adaptive character or type.) *Reproductive adaptedness must support adaptability to external change,* because there is nothing else which might support adaptability. It is clear that external selection works only and always to leave the group adapted to present and local conditions, by cutting off everything not so adapted during growth. But the adaptable group is one that continues to produce, in each generation, individuals adapted to conditions which do not now, but may later, prevail. These individuals must be of diverse adaptive types if the group is to be adaptable to different possibilities of external change; and they must be numerous enough, in each sort, to establish their type and to regenerate the group under new external conditions. *Thus, the adaptable group is that which continues to produce in each successive generation a wide variety of externally adaptive type;* it must therefore be of a certain genic structure, made up of individual genic constitutions which condition a wide variety of heritable adaptive development. This is the only alternative to the impossible hypothesis that the environment works with foreknowledge of what is to come, like an omniscient deity, and changes the genes so that they will determine developments adaptive to future conditions. (As a matter of fact, the old concept of natural selection, today displaced by genetics, was historically derived from medieval theology, which attributed the course of all particular occurrence to God's "selection" of those "eternal possibilities of existence" which he saw fit to realize. In truth, the only "eternal possibilities" are those defined by particular necessity, as we saw in an earlier chapter. For empirical science, "possibility" means partial knowledge, all occurrence being in fact particularly necessitated. We know that the sun will rise tomorrow, but we do not know whether it will be visible; so we say, "The sun may possibly shine tomorrow." But whether the sun will shine or not is even now rigorously determined, although we humans may be unable to "determine," i.e. correctly predict, the fact.)

External selection, which is *the tendency of presently adapted individuals to establish their adaptive type,* works to narrow the range of adaptive diversity in the group, and to produce a population ever more closely and uniformly adapted to *existing* conditions. External selection is what makes and keeps groups fixated. But it is not difficult to see how group selection, or reciprocal reproductive adaptedness, makes and keeps a group adaptable to external change. The better reproductively adapted are more fertile. They tend to reproduce their more fertile type, so that the fecundity of the group is constantly heightened, and progressively more progeny are produced. The more progeny, the greater the number of new genic constitutions resulting from gene exchange, the wider the individual variety of genic and adaptive type, the more adaptable the group to new and different conditions. Thus, the adaptable group is largely Rg, and contains much highly fertile type; but it cannot also be uniformly Eg, because

many of its members must have genic constitutions determining developments not well adapted to prevailing conditions, in that they are better adapted to other than
prevailing conditions. The adaptable group, we conclude,
is not a well adapted group, i.e. a group which is uniformly
RgEg. The adaptable group will rather be RgEpg, fertile,
but containing much Ep type conditioning poor externally
adaptive development. The adaptable group will be highly
persistent, because it contains a sufficiency of Eg type, conditioning present adaptedness, and also of Ep type of many
sorts, some of which will secure adaptedness to future
conditions. Change of conditions may convert Eg into Ep
type, and convert certain sorts of Ep into Eg type. E is
relative to changing external conditions whereas R is
not.

The groups which compose *species* are well adapted
groups. They are descended from ancestral groups which,
because of their superior adaptedness, increased apace, and
dissociated again and again into many separate associated
groups. (This separation need not be absolute, there may
be some gene exchange.) Let us call a *phylad* any plurality of
cognate groups descended from an identical ancestral
group. The groups composing such a phylad may proceed
along parallel lines, with little change of genic structure
or with similar change, or they may diverge to follow different routes of evolutionary change. If they remain closely
similar in their genic structure and adaptive type, we call
the phylad a "species." If they importantly diverge in type,
we may call the phylad a genus, or even a family or order.
Some species are larger than some genera, and contain more
groups. On the other hand, a single isolated group, if it is
closely similar to no other group, may be called a "rare species." There are phylads of specific, generic, and higher taxonomic status. The taxonomist is more interested in sharply

differentiated type, facilitating specification, than in the genealogy of type.

The abundant species is made up of many well adapted groups. These are not adaptable groups, but are fixated. They are the descendants of a more adaptable ancestral group which became fixated, and also highly or favorably adapted, as the result of exceptionally advantageous *genic combination*. The type of genic constitution carrying such genic combination conditioned a type of adaptive development at once fertile and exceptionally well adapted to external conditions. As this genic type was reproduced, established, and brought to dominance in the group—all other types being progressively eliminated as relatively worse adapted—the group became increasingly fecund, increased apace, spread abroad, and became dissociated into many similar cognate groups. In other words, it became a large phylad. At the same time, it became fixated as the result of the increasing lack of adaptive diversity due to the elimination of all less favored types. This increase could continue until the phylad had multiplied to fill the habitat to which it was favorably adapted, and to merit taxonomic distinction as a "species."

It is not difficult to see how genic combinations of this sort can and must continually occur in every group. In some degree, all adaptive development and character is genically combined. The genes of the individual organism are tied together in one identical genic constitution; they condition one and the same individual development; and the several developments of adaptive character condition one another, so that the failure of one development may somewhat affect all other development. However, the genic combinations of different developments may be *more* or *less close,* in part because the genes are located in a number of separate chromosomes. Developments depending on genes in the same chromosome are more closely combined in this way than developments conditioned by genes in different chromosomes. Moreover, the genes of one chromosome are likely to be transmitted together, so that *types* of genic combination are quickly established in the group. We are especially interested in just one type of genic combination; namely, that by which good reproductive development is closely combined with the development of some advantageous external adaptation.

If adequate reproductive development is genically combined with some exceptionally favorable externally adaptive development, this genic combination will tend to reproduce its type, to establish its type in the group, and in time to *dominate* the group. Not only is it favored both by reproductive and by external selection, but the genic combination helps to secure the transmittal of both adaptive types together. It is known that chromosomal aberrations occur, changing the distribution of genes in chromosomes. When this occurs, what was more closely combined becomes less closely combined, and a new close combination appears. Doubtless, new genic combinations of a highly favorable sort occur only infrequently; but where one does occur its advantage is so great that it is likely to reproduce and establish its type and come to dominance in the group. What we call a *"species" is usually a large phylad resulting from advantageous genic combination* of reproductive with some externally adaptive development.

But why should such genic combination induce fixation? First, because the combined development so established is at once highly advantageous and sure of transmittal, so that it eliminates other adaptive type. Secondly, because the type so established is a very special type, being created by the multiplication, with minimal individual difference, of a single individual genic character. Thus groups and phylads so established are bound to be exceptionally uniform, clustering closely around some norm of good adaptation. There will be in such groups a minimum of that diversity of adaptive development which makes for adaptability. And it must not be forgotten that this close uniformity and consequent fixation holds of reproductive adaptation, as well as of external adaptation. What is selected is the combined compound adaptive type, reproductive and external. Let us designate this type Rg-Egx (hyphenated). The symbol x stands for the special externally adaptive development which is genically combined with good or adequate reproductive development. The combination may be of a narrower or wider functional development. It may combine fertility with some glandular condition determining slow or rapid bodily growth, or with a more special adaptive character, such as hearing or hairiness, or with a set of special characters. Its consequence in fixation depends less on the type of adaptation than on the fact that the adaptive type, whatever it be, multiplies an *individual* character with only very slight variation, and tends to eliminate all other diversity of type in the group. *It makes the group subject to one individual,* the progenitor of its adaptive type.

This fixated type is vulnerable in two ways. First, the genic combination directly conditions *development* rather than the mature character which terminates the development. After this advantageous type has dominated the group, the development may become so accentuated as to constitute hyperdevelopment, terminating in maladaptation. Reproductive adaptation still leaves the type fertile, but ever fewer individuals of the type reach maturity. At last, too few are produced to maintain their type, and the group becomes extinct. If this hyperdevelopment occurs in all of the groups of the large phylad established in virtue of the combination in its initial, advantageous phase, the extinction may be that of a species; and extinction may occur quite rapidly, after millennia of prosperous increase. But secondly, every group so fixated by genic combination is dependent upon external stability for its persistence. It is highly adapted to *present* conditions. Its destiny is not within itself, like that of the adaptable group. There are more extinct than existing species, and in the persistent species many genic combinations must occur which carry groups to slow or rapid extinction. The number of existing groups must be a small fraction indeed of those constantly established, and usually destroyed, in the ceaseless provision of adaptive novelty secured by gene exchange.

But what preserves the adaptable group from fixation by advantageous genic combination? It is questionable whether more than a few adaptable groups ever were preserved. Possibly only one was indefinitely preserved. But, so long as *the adaptable group* persists, it *owes its persistence to high fertility not secured by close genic combination* of the type Rg-Egx. Where this type is not dominant, the distribution of adaptive character in the progeny remains random, and each generation contains much variant adaptive type. Where the type Rg-Egx is dominant, increase of fertility means increase only of the type Rg-Egx, most uniform in external adaptation. Higher fertility means greater uniformity, not less.

Little is known of the causes of chromosomal inversion and other aberrations, and of how genic character is affected by the bodily habitat of the genes in the organism. Retrospect upon the whole evolution of reproductive adaptation suggests that behind all progress of adaptive organ and tissue lies the evolution of *associative habit,* which determines how organisms are brought together, which to which, in genic mixis. But that a tremendous evolution of group adaptation occurred, securing heightened fertility, is evident enough. The fixated species fixate different phases, earlier or later, of this reproductive progress; and there has been not only continuous, but accelerated, evolution of all type, indicating a progress of adaptability itself.

The foregoing paragraphs have called attention, first, to the *group* as the vehicle of persistent or changing type. There are, strictly speaking, only associated groups. Species, genera, families, orders, classes, and phyla are *types*, not effective actualities. Each of these categories is a sort of type, narrower or wider, of group character. However, the classification of types as specific, generic, etc. does indicate the *genealogy* of groups, so classified as of identifiable type. All existing groups are of the same age in the sense that all are descended from the group that established life, with which they are *materially* continuous. But they are of different ages with respect to group type, in that they arose by dissociation, and in the great majority of cases by dissociation following special genic combination and fixation, at some precise date in the past. Each species, genus, etc. had an origin or dated beginning because each type, even the first, had its origin in some individual difference. *The actual evolution is the genealogy of groups, with type persisting or changing in each group.*

Secondly, emphasis is placed on *group adaptation,* reciprocal, reproductive, *internal to the group,* measured by *fertility* in the individual and by *fecundity* in the group. If the genealogy is that of groups, then the basic adaptation is that which binds, reproduces, and preserves groups. *All external adaptation is secondary and auxiliary*. External adaptation persists because it preserves the group between successive genic mixes, or exchanges of genes, without which nothing living persists. It is through this emphasis upon group adaptation that genetic science turns inside out, like a glove, the earlier conception which put all its emphasis upon external adaptation. If we still want to say that evolution is the result of "natural selection" working upon "individual variations," we must have chiefly in mind the *internal selection working within the group,* and working upon individual differences of *reproductive adaptation.* For without fertility, and all its conditions, there is neither persistence nor evolution of any group or type. *The evolution of life is accordingly an evolution of associative patterns,* binding individuals into groups and thereby giving persistence not to the individual but to the group. This is what we have to learn, in all its implications. Only the group persists.

To those who object that the above analysis is oversimplified, there is but one answer. It is indeed oversimplified; but any analysis of nature must first be oversimplified, if we are to see large design, allowing us to proceed to see detail. Every scientific analysis remains always oversimplified, in the necessity it is under of dealing with particulars as indices of types. But much of the complexity of contemporary biology is pseudocomplexity; it is confusion in the mind, and not complexity in nature. It arises from the impossible effort to make external selection explain what only reproductive selection can explain, and readily does explain.

The origin of species is found in those individual genic combinations Rg-Egx which established favored but fixated adaptive types. The classification of species is accordingly a classification of genic combinations of this type. But what of the origin of genera, families, orders, classes, phyla? The groups which *now* compose a genus are those of fixated species, a genus being one or more species. Nevertheless, there were once, and we must hope there still are, nonfixated adaptable groups, which did or might establish new species, new genera, new families, etc. The evolution of specific and wider type is our clue to the evolution of reproductive adaptation and fecundity, with its buttress in external adaptation.

The basic progress of life is quantitative. It is the increase of life itself, a minute group of microscopic individuals having become the massive life now on this planet. This quantitative progress was conditioned by a qualitative progress of adaptive character and type, especially of group adaptation. However, the whole progress was a long chain reaction. *The increase of life,* conditioned by reproductive adaptation, *was itself the major external change* which made readaptation, biotic and physical, the condition of group persistence; and such biotic readaptation required group readaptation, which might induce either fixation or widened adaptability. The species tell us of readaptations bought at the price of fixation. They tell us nothing directly of the major, epoch-making readaptations which created the enormous phylads which are phyla, classes, and orders. Nor does the paleontological record mention those adaptable groups which founded the great dynasties of life. Its whole record is of large fixated species, either still existing or extinct. Nor is it surprising that there is no record of those "missing links." Only with man was the adaptable group a group at once capable of great increase and secured against external change. Prior to man, the adaptable group was a group poorly adapted to external conditions, maintaining itself by good group adaptation and high fertility, decimated in every generation by mortality during growth, paying the full price for its diversity of adaptive type. The adaptable group was small, harassed, bedeviled by circumstance, obscure. But, one by one, it seems, adaptable groups succumbed to fixation, capitalizing on their principal, and leaving only that single line of progress which proceeds from the group which originated life to the group which established primitive man. The adaptable group came to its high estate at last, to start a new epoch in the evolution of the world.

The classification of specific type is primarily a classification of external adaptation; but the classification of type becomes one of reproductive adaptation when we mount to its higher stages, in the classes and phyla.

Life was initiated by a reproductive readaptation. This was the adaptation which separated genic substance from other protoplasm, establishing the habit of genic mixis or gene exchange, condition of all that lives. A second major readaptation was that which gathered genic substance into the nucleus, protecting the genes and freeing the cytoplasm for diverse external readaptation. There was an evolution of mobile habit with rudimentary locomotive organs in these unicellular groups, presumably as a group adaptation supporting syngamy and the process of genic mixis. The protozoa advanced to protosexual differentiation, allowing genes of different type to be retained in the group, thus widening adaptability. The advance to the protozoic colony was initially an associative readaptation, allowing the functional differentiation of cells, which later led to multicellular organization proper. This progress repeats on a much larger scale the earlier readaptation establishing cellular type, with inexhaustible diversity of external adaptation and adaptive organ and tissue. The advance to bisexuality was then completed. It made the genic substance a reservoir of latent adaptive diversity, available on demand of changed conditions. It is this adaptation that gives to most fixated species such adaptability as they retain. The plants achieved multicellular form at much sacrifice of mobility and associative habit, so that their major evolution was checked. Some plants secured a vicarious mobility by symbiotic adaptation with animal carriers of seed; but this tied persistence, and any further evolution, to external adaptation depending on other species. In the multicellular animals, however, association remained mobile. Each major reproductive adaptation set the stage for a tremendous evolution of external readaptation, this either fixating the type or conditioning further associative group adaptation. Thus, there was an evolution of powerful locomotive organs as externally adaptive mechanisms, so that the group became highly mobile. This adaptation could persist only if associative habit was much strengthened to keep the mobile group together, or to reassemble it, in the interests of gene exchange. *This intensified associative bond integrating highly mobile groups finally conditioned that familiar but still almost incredible progress which led through the higher animals to man.*

The evolution of type in plants and the lower animals was supported chiefly by means of heightened individual fertility, securing adaptability to external change. Adaptability was thus obtained by open embrace of external selection, the group exposing to the environment the widest possible range of externally adaptive diversity. Necessarily, most of this diverse character was maladapted to existing conditions; and as fertility was heightened, mortality became enormous, only a few of the millions of progeny reaching maturity. Much more effective in securing gene exchange and persistence of the group would be any adaptation which would insulate the growing generation from external selection, so that not the second generation merely, but the third, was secured. Such an escape from "external selection" could be provided only by "associative selection." More properly stated, associative adaptation would somehow have to replace external adaptation, and do service for it.

This covered tunnel, protecting the group in its passage from one genic mixis to the next, was provided by parental protection leading to *domesticity*. Highly mobile fish had become strongly gregarious, traveling long distances to the breeding grounds, the males attending the females individually, protecting the nests, and moving in some cases to *individual fertilization* of the eggs within the female, the progeny being then delivered mobile. This direction was followed further in the amphibia, reptiles, and mammals. Incubation became gestation, and this was steadily lengthened. Warm-bloodedness then came to accelerate the process. The progeny were nourished, guarded, and educated after birth. This period of infancy was steadily lengthened, until it overlapped several breeding seasons, so that progeny of different ages grew up together. The family was established.

A group that brings all its progeny to reproductive maturity would not need to be externally adapted nor adaptable, since it is insulated from environmental selection. Yet it would, in fact, be highly adaptable, because its "genic pool" would indefinitely retain all diversity of type that arose. The group that brings an increasing proportion of progeny to maturity is assured of widening adaptability, and also, of course, of persistence. High fertility is here less needed. Fertility was in consequence steadily lowered as parental protection increased, the individual young receiving greater protection in individual care. Thus evolved domesticity, born of the association which had always conditioned gene exchange, and which was now extended from the adult generation to the progeny. With this associative readaptation began the evolution of *mind,* leading to that of *society* and the *intellect*.

Let us try to summarize this account of evolutionary progress. There appeared a single living group, persisting in virtue of its group adaptation conditioning gene exchange and external adaptability. This living group persisted from generation to generation, conserving its adaptability through every change of adaptive type. That *identical* group proceeded through an evolution of adaptive type, becoming protozoa, porifera, coelenterata, and on to become chordata, craniata, pisces, amphibia, reptilia, mammalia, primate, anthropoid, human. It was an Rg Egp (unhyphenated) group, *never fixated by genic combination,* or fixated to a minimum degree. It was of all groups the best associated, the most fecund, the most adaptable to external change. It maintained fecundity by means of high individual fertility, until in the vertebrates it secured group fecundity by parental protection, with low individual fertility. *It was never, until it became man, an externally well adapted group.* It paid for its persistence the highest price paid by any group that exists today, or that ever did exist.

That single group, numbering possibly at certain times only a few dozen or a few hundred individuals, and secured at any and every time by individual variants of adaptive type, *is the trunk line of evolution.* From it diverged, by minor or major fixation of adaptive type, all other groups. Such devolution was irreversible, the established fixation being permanent. The adaptable group alone retained its reproductive association under continual external readaptation. It alone evolved. All other groups devolved, becoming dependent on external adaptedness for persistence, not only for individual survival. The adaptable group is the sole group which never became dependent upon the environment *for its persistence. It never sacrificed the next generation,* and with this all future generations, *to the present generation. It alone controlled and controls its destiny.*

We therefore conclude that the evolution of all living types—species, genera, families, orders, classes, and phyla—was primarily the work of group selection, working in the association internal to the group, and only secondarily aided by the work of external selection. More properly, it was the work of group adaptation or association, endangered and almost everywhere overborne by external selection, i.e. the need of external adaptation. The species are only the raveled fringe of the shawl of life. The pattern of the shawl is that of the progressively fixated groups which established phylads of the rank of phyla, classes, orders, families, and genera. *But the weaver of the shawl is no part of it. It is that group which became mankind.* Man is not, and never was, a species, a genus, a type. When man to himself is true, he is the group which created all specific and other type.

* 4 *

THE KEY IN THE LOCK

EVOLUTIONARY science, implemented by population genetics, inaugurates a new intellectual era because it shows all persistence of type (form, structure) to be the index of the persistence of groups, secured by associative adaptation. We must learn the whole implication and consequence of this epochal discovery. The task can best be begun by discovering why scientists and philosophers so long neglected the "facts of life," i.e. the *adaptive character of all type and structure*.

The Darwinian evolutionist overemphasized external adaptation, and neglected group adaptation, in order to avoid vitalism and Aristotelian metaphysics. Before Darwin, and since Aristotle, all persistence of adaptive type had been ascribed to "eternal specific forms," which were believed to direct the "normal" individual development to its proper goal in adult adaptation. The species were supposedly "fixed"; and their fixity was "explained" by saying that there are just so many "eternal specific forms," directing just so many sorts of individual developments, and consequently securing the persistence of just so many species. The "specific form" was believed to secure all normal adaptive development, both reproductive and external. However, this fallacy of "specific forms" did call attention to reproductive adaptation, reproductive development assuring that organisms will mate within their species and breed true. The

[55]

fallacy is not, of course, the belief in specific types as such. Individuals really are similar or different in respect to specific type. The fallacy is the belief that specific type is a causal agency, that specific type maintains itself by its action upon individual developments. In fact, of course, it is individuals that maintain (or change) type, not type that maintains individuals. But to explain how individuals, none of which persists, can maintain persistent type, we need to see the actuality of the group, which alone actually persists, here keeping and there changing its type.

The Darwinian scientist firmly rejected the dogma of "fixed species" and the fallacy of causally effective "specific forms." He saw clearly that any change of specific type (origin of species) is conditioned by the variant individual organisms themselves. He rightly concluded that something else than the variant individuals conditions the persistence of type, and is at work when types, not merely individuals, change. In ignorance of population genetics and of group adaptation, he thought always of the persistence or change of *specific* type; and since he could not appeal to "specific forms," working from within the species, he placed the species in the context of the environment, and tried to explain all persistence and change of type as the result of environmental persistence and change. This focused attention wholly upon external adaptation to environmental conditions; and the fiction of environmental or external "selection" was adduced to make good the neglect of group adaptation, gene exchange, and fertility as the causal factors determining evolutionary progress. It was believed that such complete reliance upon the environment, and even upon the physical environment, as the director of evolutionary progress protected mechanistic science from the vitalist and the theologian, who wanted to perpetuate the fallacy of effective "specific forms"; but, as was pointed out, the notion that the environment "selects" certain variants threw the thinker back upon theological metaphor, covered up lacunae of causal explanation, and prevented mechanistic description.

Fortunately, the concepts of the group and of group adaptation remove these lacunae and allow causal explanation. The biologist can now do justice to the partial truth of Aristotelian vitalism, which did serve to remind us of the reciprocal reproductive adaptation which conditions group persistence, although it mistook this adaption, truly internal to the group, as intraspecific. But the notion of "natural selection by the environment" seemed to be admirably naturalistic, empirical, scientific, and to bring biology closer to the physical sciences, or even within physical science, by suggesting that evolutionary progress is only a local and rather peculiar manifestation of physical nature, which here causally determines the persistence or change of organic type. This suggestion was doubly pernicious; first, because it deflected attention from all adaptive character whatsoever; secondly, because it returned to vitalism in its implication that all living adaptation is only a somewhat special manifestation of the power of physical type to establish and maintain itself. The "laws of evolution," it was vaguely supposed, are a local specification of the physical necessity which maintains all physical structure in the universe. Evolutionary progress, the continual change of adaptive type, was deprecated as merely a minor instance of the persistence of physical structure. The persistence of physical structure itself was taken for granted, i.e. it was taken to be "natural necessity." But any such supposition of *necessary structure* in nature is metaphysical fiction, and quite nonempirical, in that it requires the denial of *particular* causation, the sole effective causation in nature. This supposition is only a sort of universal vitalism, appealing to an "eternal physical structure" instead of a plurality of "specific forms." It is a refusal of evolutionary science, which denies the eternity of every type and structure, and proposes to discover the origin of types and structures in "individual variations."

So far from being determined by the physical environment, the evolution of life has proceeded with very little change of physical adaptation, strictly understood. Some of the oldest species are very well adapted, and are living today; and every group that lives today has remained, ever since its origin, sufficiently adapted physically. The physical environment is in fact remarkably stable and uniform. Diversities of climate and terrain require diverse physical adaptation; and the spread of life from some point of origin to cover the globe required some physical readaptation. However, this spread was most directly conditioned by increase, depending upon group and biotic adaptation. It is questionable whether there has been major readaptation directly due to temporal *change* of the physical environment. Consider the evolution of marine animals and plants, issuing in multitudinous genera and species, which arose in the most stable physical environment known or conceivable!

Much more important than "physical selection" has been "biotic selection," i.e. the tendency of good biotic adaptation to establish its type. (Much of what is called "physical adaptation" is really biotic or associative adaptation. For example, fins, wings, and other locomotive adaptations are associative adaptations supporting gene exchange, or biotic adaptations supporting the pursuit of food. Physical adaptation conditions *all* adaptation, and therefore does not usually explain differences of adaptive type.) The evolution of biotic adaptation kept groups divergent in type ecologically related, so that they maintained a loose organic economy. It should not be forgotten that all biotic adaptation, adapting the individual of any living group to members of other living groups, is ultimately derived from the group adaptation which associated the members of the first living group. This group had no neighbors, and consequently no biotic adaptation. When it became dissociated to form a phylad of many groups, its associative pattern became the biotic adaptations interrelating the cognate groups. The ecological pattern which makes of living matter a loose economy of species is the descendant of the group adaptation which established life. The "instincts" of animals, adapting animal habit to the biotic environment, may help us to understand the group association in which all such habit originated.

Grounding all progress of external adaptation was the progress of group adaptation, which conditioned, and was in turn reconditioned by, all external readaptation. The periods of warm and moist climate were periods of great evolutionary change. They were so because this stability of favorable physical conditions supported great increase, which changed biotic conditions and so set the stage for biotic readaptations. Both increase and biotic re-adaptation induce further group readaptation. The congested populations exert new and intensified pressures upon their own members, and thus condition the establishment and persistence of new adaptive type, supporting an increasing population within the same geographical habitat. However, changed conditions effected evolution of new adaptive type only where, and in the degree that, groups remained adaptable in virtue of good group adaptation and high fertility. The basic evolution is not that of species, although it is disclosed by the classification of species. What the classification discloses is the evolution of associative pattern, group adaptation, and reproductive fertility, together with steady departure from adaptability, under increasing external pressure, into fixated specific type. The associative bond, securing the persistence of the group under increasing pressure, has been steadily strengthened, until today the association which held together the microscopic organisms of a minute group has become an association able to maintain the persistence, and to secure the increase, of all that lives.

Except for Darwin's studies of "sexual selection," seldom further pursued, little attention has been devoted to associative habit. The existence of this habit is observable in mobile populations, where it brings individuals together, or prevents the mobile group from disintegration, to permit gene exchange. But the seeds of plants, too, are so reciprocally and diversely adapted that a given seed is more fertile with seed of its own group than with seed of other groups, and more fertile with this seed than with that within its own group. It is clear that all adaptive development whatsoever is basically conditioned by genic structure; and genic structure at any time is the result of the details of genic mixis or gene exchange, which in turn are determined by associative habit. Some groups of the same species occupy the same habitat, and are barely distinguishable in type, yet do not interbreed. There is hybridization between groups of different species and even of different genera. Associative habit is no respecter of specific form. But within one and the same group there is always individual difference, and continual selection of associative type. What ultimately determines all evolution of group and type is this reciprocal adaptation, better or worse, among individuals of the same group. The major factor directing evolution is not in the environment—there is nothing in the environment which resembles the pattern of species or the organic economy. Nor is the cause to be located in the species. *The cause is within the group.* It lies in the actual detail of association, in the reciprocal adaptation of this *individual* with that *individual*. This is why biological science is and must be statistical. All types, constants, "causal laws," and correlations are statistical averages and means; and what they finally present is a statistical summary of the types of association that have drawn to genic mixis pairs of individuals, which thereby reproduce, establish, and again destroy adaptive type.

Thus physical adaptation, and indeed all external adaptation, is only the table upon which proceeds evolutionary progress, that of reciprocal adaptation among individuals. It is true that organisms fall off the table, failing to reach maturity and to reproduce their individual character in type. But the table itself is largely the product of past association, which through its maintenance of living form has transformed even the mineral surface of the earth, filling the soil with water and organic matter, and making of the atmosphere a great market place for the symbiotic barter of oxygen for carbon dioxide between animals and plants.

There has been continual increase of life, supported by the continual multiplication of groups, *each of which perpetuates its distinctive associative type.* The ground floor of the classification of type is that provided by groups, each of which is distinct in associative type. The increase of life is not uniform, but proceeds in larger, smaller, and ever smaller waves. The great waves are the phyla, enormous phylads created in virtue of major associative readaptations. Smaller waves are classes, still smaller waves are orders, and so on. The waves start from a point, to cover the habitable earth or to spread through the ocean. Each wave moves over and upon the organic economy resulting from earlier waves, to establish the successful categories of its period. Thus, the first multicellular phylum submerged the protozoa, and the mammals displaced the reptiles. The movement is like that of variations upon a theme. The theme is stated by the constant requirements of physical adaptation and of organic economy. It is the pattern of external adaptive types. The variations are introduced by major associative and reproductive readaptations. There is parallelism of specific type between the unicellular and multicellular forms, between the reptiles and the mammals, etc.

The primacy of associative adaptation, i.e. its dominance over external adaptation, is required as the condition of any persistence of group or type. External adaptation secures survival of the individual to reproductive maturity. It does not secure the reproduction of type. It does not secure the persistence of group or type. Living matter persists only in virtue of gene exchange, conditioned by association. Survival, without persistence, is of no account. *The individual owes its existence, all that it is and has, to the group and its associative adaptation;* but the individual, also, in its maintenance of associative habits, is the giver of life to succeeding generations. Even the humblest type, if it is to persist, must in some degree subordinate external to reproductive adaptation, and sacrifice survival to persistence, the present to the future, the self to the group. The adaptable group makes this sacrifice in greatest degree. Life is inexpugnably temporal, snatching persistence from survival by group adaptation.

This preference of group persistence to individual survival is moral preference, whether it be conscious or not. The organic economy, resting as it does wholly upon groups and their internal adaptation, is moral economy. The more adaptable group is the better group, morally speaking. Whatever we may take to be the nature of physical matter, *living matter is subject to a natural moral law.* The group which remained adaptable, and thus became the progenitor of all that has lived and lives, is a group which never broke this moral law, requiring the sacrifice of external adaptation to group adaptation and of individual survival to group persistence. It is this same moral inclination that persists, in diluted form, in the organic economy. Thus, group genetics recovers what there was of moral insight in the vitalistic metaphysics of pre-Darwinian science; but it does this without departing from mechanistic explanation. It was the desire of the Greek metaphysician to see in nature a moral economy that led him to see in "eternal structure" the moral law of nature, requiring of each individual thing conformity to form and type. But we see that the individual is not so constrained by eternal necessity. The sole necessities are those of its own and other particular character. No "specific forms," nothing outside the living individuals themselves, constrains life to conform to type. Nevertheless, each and every individual is "good" or "bad," i.e. it is better or worse associatively adapted; and, according to its better or worse association, it will support persistence more or less, and so either sustain or destroy the group, life, and the economy of nature.

It is evident that the extinct species had but little adaptability. What shall we say of the species that exist today? They are one and all fixated, and dependent upon the persistence of the stable environmental conditions to which they are so perfectly adapted. But the increase of life, and the multiplication and complication of adaptive type, has not ceased. It has accelerated. Today, man cultivates much of the habitable earth. Another twenty thousand years, possibly much less, and man will have so increased that every continent is cultivated, and what is preserved will be by man preserved. The dry land will be man's garden, and the ocean will be his fishpond, stocked and harvested for human use. Nothing will live except by man's consent; and the abundant species will be those of man's contriving, created in the laboratory or the field by scientific experiment. What was ever adaptable, really and securely? Only that group which became man. The loose organic economy now tightens up. It becomes integral, controlled, directed. It becomes clear, today, that the evolution was always directed from within, never from outside. The association which established life is today human intelligence, comptroller and creator of the organic economy of living matter.

There is no eternal structure, and consequently there is no absolute knowledge of eternal form. But there is an empirical knowledge which becomes more sure and more true, as it steadily comprehends more of the past. An evolutionary science moves from the present to the past, and back again. By causal inference and imaginative hypothesis it makes present observable fact the datum allowing knowledge of past fact. *All science is* this retrospective *natural history*. But this knowledge of the past then allows understanding of the present, which is now known as the causal outcome of the past. Thus, there is no authentic knowledge of this time or that time; but all knowledge is of all the history known. We can understand the evolution of life mechanistically only if we understand earlier phases causally, in terms of their later effects; and we understand life as it is today only by knowing it as the issue of that past. We comprehend the evolution of life in its entirety when we know that the association which first established life has since created all that has lived, and that this association is today the kinship which makes of humanity *mankind,* an associated or kin group. Man is not and never was a species. He persisted, and must still persist, only as a group, integrated by the reciprocal adaptations of individuals.

* 5 *

TURNING THE KEY

THE concepts of group persistence and group adaptation provide the key to the evolution of life, both in its long history and in its last phase, that of human progress. With this key, we may clarify the philosophical issues which divide men, by following them to their sources in divergent directions of evolutionary change. Knowing the issues clearly in their sources, we can intelligently resolve them. We proceed, therefore, from the survey of the earlier evolution of adaptive type, leading to parental protection and domesticity, to a survey of the evolution of the human group.

We saw that domesticity went far toward insulating the group from external selection. It secured persistence through two generations, and allowed group adaptation to do what had always been done by external adaptation. The time came when a group was so far secured from external selection that it no longer needed to be adaptable to *external* change. Here was a group, at last, which could increase without the help of genic combinations assuring adaptation but destroying adaptability. Of what value was adaptability to a group no longer subject to external selection?

There is group adaptation and external adaptation. Consequently, there is fixation and adaptability with respect to group adaptation, as well as with respect to external adaptation. There proceeded among the animals a great evolution of reproductive type, with heightening fertility. There was "selection" of better reproductive adaptation, and elimination of worse. This was *selection internal to the group.* Some groups advanced, and others did not advance, to individual fertilization, prolonged gestation, warm-bloodedness, mammalian nurture; and, in the groups which advanced through this progress, some individuals were more, and others less, advanced in type. Genic combinations may occur to fixate all adaptive type, reproductive as well as external. Internal adaptability was needed if there was to be further evolution of group adaptation and association. The evolution of the vertebrates is very obviously one of reproductive and associative type. Did it not issue in human society? There are today human groups relatively fixated, and other groups very adaptable and progressive, in social habit. Similarly, there were vertebrate groups more fixated or more adaptable in their domestic and other reproductive adaptation.

Domesticity was initially an agency of gene exchange and group persistence; but it had two by-products of epochal significance. The first was its consequence in *the transmittal of acquired character,* supplementing that of genic type. The development of the progeny was deeply shaped by the domestic environment. The individual responded to the stimulus of parental attention with *filial* response. When the young came to maturity, their response to their progeny was a modified recall of the earlier filial response. Thus, the parental type of domestic habit was transmitted to and through the growing progeny. The two parents, furthermore, coming from different families, brought together two variant types of domestic habit. There is something comparable to gene exchange in this fusion and diversified recombination in several progeny of maternal and paternal domestic types, each child drawing from either parent a somewhat different response, and being differently stimulated in its associative development. The domestic upbringing then determined to a high degree the reciprocal choice of mate. The sterile human is often the child for whom parental affection was too weak, aberrant, or intense, so that it implanted a type of domestic habit which cannot fuse with that of a mate. The sins of parents are still visited upon the children, even to the third and fourth generation. Biologically sound in psychoanalysis is its attention to filial relationship as a controlling factor in individual destiny, for good as for evil.

The second great by-product of domestic habit was its *socialization of the group*. The child in the family gave and received *fraternal* response. Fraternity later conditioned his adult response to those outside the family but within the mating group. The domesticated group steadily became a socialized group, bound by fraternal affection and respect, by piety toward the older, and by protective care of the younger. The true society is a large quasi-domestic group, in which domestic affection is brought by each to all. *Socialization widens domestic association to cover the group.*

These two by-products of domesticity, securing the transmission of *acquired* character first domestically and then socially, are the substance of the *human mind*. The "mind" is acquired type, transmitted and individuated. In primitive humanity, each group had its own "mind," a distinctive type of transmitted associative habit peculiar to that group. (The "human intellect" is a later amplification of this group "mind.") Thus, the mind is a cause and index of group persistence, and of the persistence and change of adaptive type.

Primitive man is believed to have originated a quarter of a million years ago, and to have endured until the rise of civilized societies some seven or ten thousand years ago. The group in which man originated probably knew domestic protection for six or seven years; but infancy was now lengthened, maturation was steadily postponed, the family endured longer, until childhood covered some fourteen or more years, allowing long development in acquired habit. The progress of primitive man was advanced by the continual extension of domestic response to the group. As the group became more socialized, it afforded greater protection to the adult individual and the family. As the family became stronger, and endured longer, it deepened its influence upon individual development, and so more effectively socialized the group, which then still better protected the family, and so on. This *repercussion between domestic and social habit* was, and still is, *the dynamo of human progress.* But the evolution of primitive man was very different from our own civilized progress. It was still, like animal evolution, radiant or dispersive. The group which became man increased in the strength of its domestic adaptation, retaining adaptability. It spread, dissociated, and became a great phylad of small groups moving over the habitable earth. These highly adaptable groups underwent minor readaptations to diverse habitats and to local fauna and flora. Their increase was finally checked by the limitations of natural food resources. They were little subject to external selection, but highly susceptible to internal selection; and there was great divergence and rapid evolution of associative type, domestic and social. After primitive man had reached the limits of his natural resources, neighboring groups came into competition for terrain, hunting and fishing rights, etc.; and there began an evolution of heritable acquired habit which repeats, with significant differences, the earlier animal evolution of genic type.

The animal group was given its adaptability to external conditions (biotic and physical) by its internal adaptation securing fecundity. The primitive human group met its most important external environment in neighboring human populations. It developed types of acquired character, induced by domestic and social education, which adapted its members internally to one another, and externally to neighboring human groups. Domestic and social habit was supplemented by military training, inducing belligerent habit and enabling the group to compete for natural resources. Each group evolved its peculiar *cult*, a pattern of domestic and social habit supporting the group economy, transmitted by education, inducing amicability and loyalty within the group but developing courage or belligerence toward competitive neighbors. This cultural pattern could become fixated, much as genic type had been fixated, by the dominance of advantageous adaptive combinations. There was an evolution of acquired cultural type, with fixation of type, extinction of type, or continued adaptability to external change.

We may call the primitive human group a *clan*. Each clan had its small, self-sufficient, domestic and social *economy*, i.e. its transmitted type of acquired habit adapting the individual first to his own group, secondly to other human groups, and thirdly to animals, plants, and the physical habitat. We may overlook the evolution of biotic and physical adaptation in man, conceiving the nonhuman environment to be stable, in view of the rapidity and importance of the evolution of acquired habit in man. The primitive clan became a small but highly organized group, the individual being completely regulated in behavior and habit by the associative type of his clan. He did not distinguish his individual identity from the identity of the clan. He thought, lived, hunted, fished, feasted, starved, slept, mated, prospered, and perished as a member of the clan. Toward the members of other clans he brought the habitual response induced by his upbringing within his own clan.

Intense competition induced warlike habit, the young being educated primarily in military virtues. This cultivation of fierceness was not without influence upon domestic character and type. The clan could become so habituated to war that domestic and social affection suffered, and so geared to war that the social economy failed. The fate of each clan was determined by its clan cult, which was to acquired habit what the "gene-pool" is to heritable genic type. Some fixation of cultural pattern was inevitable, in that the integrity of the clan, i.e. its persistence as a group, depended upon the preservation and transmission of cultural habit. But the clan could be more or less culturally fixated, and more or less responsive in its habits to *changes* among neighboring populations. It could be so conditioned by external pressure that it became ferocious and aggressive, losing its domestic and social habit, sacrificing its internal economy, ceasing to reproduce itself, and finally becoming extinct. It could strike a balance between internal and external adaptation, so that it persisted and prospered as long as conditions did not appreciably change. Or it could remain culturally plastic, modifying its cultural habit in response to external change, and advancing cultural progress. Just as the fixation or adaptability of genically transmitted type depends on the interplay of group adaptation and external adaptation, so the fixation or adaptability of cultural habit depends on this interplay. But group adaptation is in man the extension of domestic response to embrace the group. It is the quasi-domestication of the group. *The adaptable so-*

ciety was consequently that which preserved, and continually strengthened, domestic association and the family; in this is the source of all human association and human peace.

It is instructive to contrast human sociability with that of the so-called "social insects." These are in fact very highly *domesticated* insects, the insect colony being a large family, progeny of a single fertilized "queen." Here, domestic adaptation virtually insulates the growing generation, brought up in the hive, from external selection; and the colony is assured of persistence. However, the domestic service is provided through the intense specialization and sterilization of all but a few of the progeny; and only one pair of each generation ordinarily comes to genic mixis. This leaves the colony completely fixated as to type, the diversity of adaptive type being reduced to the absolute minimum compatible with persistence. These domestic insects entered an evolutionary blind alley; and we can see that their error was to achieve domesticity at the price of group association. *In establishing the family, they destroyed the group.*

Vertebrate domesticity was achieved at less cost. All the progeny remained fertile, and the group became a plurality of small families, associative or group adaptation being retained along with domestic habit. This conditioned the repercussion between domestic and social units, i.e. between the family and the mating group, which advanced human progress, this being a domestic and a social evolution at once. The fixation of the domesticated insects was due to a hyperdevelopment of domestic habit, destroying group association. But the contrary error, the development of social habit at the expense of domesticity, is also possible; and it is the error to which the human group is most susceptible.

The primitive human societies which remained adaptable were those which preserved strong domesticity, so that there persisted the variety of domestic type which secures wide variety of individual acquired character. This diversity prevented the fixation of the adult population in cultural orthodoxy and social uniformity. *The individual variations which advance social evolution are those of diverse adaptive character acquired in the family,* as the result of diverse filial relationship and domestic development. These individual characters the adult carries with him into the social group, where they influence social association and modify cultural type.

The development of the civilized human individual today covers three phases, indicative of the past evolution of human type. The first phase covers five or seven years of *infancy,* leading to a false adolescence, which is quickly suppressed in order to postpone full maturation for some seven or eight years of *childhood.* The false adolescence is physiologically reminiscent of the prehuman group, which matured at this age, before the evolution of the primitive human family doubled the length of childhood. Postponement of adolescence allows the full development of domestic and social adaptation, i.e. of acquired habit; but it also makes childhood, and especially adolescence, difficult and even precarious, because of the inhibition of sexual response as the result of domestic and cultural pressure, which censors precocious development. Each child still pays for his human estate, his mature status being that which he bought by inner conflict during childhood and growth. However, childhood varies tremendously among different families and different social groups, according to the degree of evolution of domestic and group type. Here, development is easier; there, it is more difficult, its past course being deducible from adult behavior. There are atavistic societies today, still of low primitive type, where little inhibition exists, and growth is correspondingly easy and unproductive, the adults being still children. There are minority groups in civilized society where growth is extremely difficult, and correspondingly productive of adult development. There are those in civilized society whose growth is substantially primitive in type. There are men who fill sports arenas, make themselves the dupes of chauvinist leaders, identify themselves with some local "fraternity" perpetuating a primitive cult; and there are women of narrow and easily exhausted domestic interest, who quickly turn to the support of "social" clubs and aimless gregariousness. Adult character, determining group destiny, is itself determined in infancy and childhood, first in the family, but increasingly in the conflict within the individual between domestic and group response. The more civilized the society, the more intense become these tensions within individuals between domestic and social habits. *Human progress, both primitive and civilized, has been advanced by individuals whose family upbringing induced inner conflict leading to acquired character of new sort,* able to establish its type in the composite group culture.

The adaptable clans which advanced the progress of primitive society were those in which domestic association remained strong, keeping the group socialized and adaptable to external change. The adaptable group was of more amiable, peaceful type than that which fixated its cult in response to external pressures. Where the fixated group might destroy itself by its emphasis upon belligerent training, which kept it warlike and made it aggressive, the adaptable group extended its amicable response to peaceful neighbors. There arose economic and marital interrelations among clans, leading to the evolution of the clan system or *primitive nation,* with corresponding evolution of the clan cult into tribal culture.

In primitive society, the institution of marriage was established to preserve the integrity of the family within the increasingly socialized group. The protection afforded to the individual by the socialized group made the family less indispensable as an agency of insulation from external relation; but the family was still needed as the agency of education and of group adaptability. The institution of marriage allowed domestically acquired character to determine mating and the detail of genic mixis, so that *acquired character conditioned the further evolution of all adaptive type* whatsoever. In primitive man, through the institution of domestic and social forms, the associated group became completely and intelligently responsible for its destiny. "Mind," in associative habit and its evolution, now dominated over physiological "matter" in the genes.

Evidently, the evolution of primitive society proceeded to the establishment of sizable "nations," covering large areas and supported by quite complex interadaptations of a political-economic sort, and also of marriage customs, among local groups. But this primitive evolution was suddenly and irreversibly stopped by a new readaptation, one of revolutionary consequence. This was the *advance to the cultivation of crops and herds,* which destroyed primitive economy and initiated the advance to large civilized society.

The cultivation of crops and herds was a *biotic* readaptation, changing the relationship of the human individual to certain species of plants and animals. However, it originated in an *associative* readaptation, not incorrectly named "the domestication of animals and plants." This practice seems to have arisen in connection with the clan cult, which made use of certain plants and animals as properties in its rituals. (Some of these species continued to be used as symbols in the religious cults of civilized society.) The term "domestication" reminds us that the *protective care given to human progeny was here extended to the young of other species.*

In this way associative habit, which had controlled the whole course of plant and animal evolution, finally broke through the limits of the small associated group to bind together groups of several specific types. (The domesticated insects also domesticate and cultivate groups of other species.) With the cultivation of food resources, the human group was freed from the last natural checks upon increase which had kept it small. With cultivation, the controls of population became labor and social peace.

The earlier radiant or dispersive evolution of specific type really came to an end with the advance to the tribe or primitive nation. But cultivation carried the process much further. It so increased the groups that they overlapped, to form a huge conglomerate society which brought together a variety of group cults and a great diversity of associative habits. There began here the progress to the large society, maintaining a social economy which includes not only humans, but also plant and animal populations, preserved and modified in type by cultivation. The *progress toward civilization* was an advance to new types of associative habit, secured and transmitted by means of political, economic, vocational, marital, and other social institutions. But this progress was not automatic. It was not conditioned by the requirement of readaptation to external change (except where human activity induced such change, as in the cultivation of food and its consequences). It was an evolution of associative habit, i.e. of adaptation internal to society. *The adaptability required was that of associative habit itself.* The ground of this adaptability was the diversity of *acquired* character produced in the many families. The large society was adaptable and progressive in the degree to which acquired individual character could establish its type in the group culture, influencing the evolution of social institutions. The source of adaptability, in short, was the power of individuals to direct the course of social progress. This power is *individual freedom;* but the consequence of individual freedom depends upon the domestic and social patterns which determine individual characters.

Some seven or ten thousand years ago, then, the dispersive *evolution of genic type* was completely replaced by the *progress of acquired habit,* which must eventually bring all humanity and all other life on this planet into a great civilized economy governed by man, and controlled by means of institutions (associative habits) subject to progressive modification by new acquired character. The dispersive evolution was replaced by one which again integrated what had earlier been dispersed. This was an epochal change, inaugurating a new era of cosmic evolution. *What supports and advances this progress of civilization is properly called the human intellect.* It must be our purpose, accordingly, to understand that intellect, which makes man adaptable to the changes which he himself induces in the world, and able to persist and to increase by progressive readaptation to the changes.

Primitive "mind," or the associative habit of primitive man, was carried and transmitted in the clan cult. A good deal of primitive culture came down in modified forms into the early civilized cultures of which we have record; and there have remained fixated primitive societies to this day. Ubiquitous, apparently, was the tendency of the primitive group to preserve its identity, and to perpetuate its difference from other groups, by means of animal and plant symbols—the practice which had such enormous consequence in the "domestication" and cultivation of certain animal and plant species. The clansman identified his clan as that of the Wolf, the Horse, the Boar, the Oak, the Wheat, the Fish, etc. He devised rituals making use of individuals of these species as symbols of the clan; and he used the persistence of specific form to symbolize that of the clan as a superindividual unit. He called himself "child" of the Wolf, the Horse, and so on. He developed folklore, which made mythical animals and plants the agents of clan legend and group memory. We can intellectually understand the clan cult with its myths only as an effort of primitive man to adapt himself to the new human environment which resulted from rapid human increase, by modifying his prehuman biotic adaptations to animals and plants. The prehuman ancestors of man were closely dependent for survival and persistence upon these plant and animal species. With domesticity, sociability, and the associative readaptation of linguistic communication, the earlier pattern of biotic adaptation was transformed into this curious acquired habit, used now to transmit group adaptations. Solemn rituals initiated the "children of the Boar," or restored the adults, into the "mystery" of the life and persistence of the clan. The clansmen did not mistake myth, as did decadent mythology, for literal truth. They knew that the Boar was the life of the clan. But the myth was not less effective on that account. The clan was a jealous god, rigorous in its demands and merciless in its punishments; for it was dependent upon group integrity for its persistence, and this no longer received any environmental support but was wholly dependent upon associative habit and internal selection. The primitive symbols still have power over those who eat fish on Friday, eschew pork, enshrine holly and mistletoe, thrill to British lion or American eagle, drink the blood of the Lamb, bow to the Cross which was the sacred tree.

With the confusion of myths of clans brought together

by cultivation, there proceeded an evolution of new institutions supported by a new sort of myth, which became personalized in anthropomorphic religion. For civilized man, the wilderness with its living species was somewhat remote, and human society was seen in the larger context of physical nature. Sun, moon, and stars now come to play an important symbolic role, the human economy being interpreted as a reflection or specification of the divine economy of universal nature.

Civilized man long remembered in his legends his earlier primitive economy, the "Garden of Eden" where he had received his sustenance directly from nature, and from which cultivation had ejected him, to earn his bread henceforth by knowledge of plant and animal growth, by labor, and with the sweat of his brow. Nor would he ever cease to be nostalgic for primitive community and. innocence. Especially when civilization came into stress would he dream of a "return to nature."

But his immediate business was always the creation of a new and larger myth, supporting the institutions of a growing civilized economy. Professional priesthoods arose, devoting themselves to this readaptive work. Expected to preserve orthodox myth, they inevitably proceeded to refashion myth. With control by cultivation, awe in face of the clan symbols was complicated by the desire to control the natural agencies which condition growth and increase. The ritual inevitably tended to become magic, securing along with group persistence its conditions in the health of crops and herds. The awe felt before nature was transferred in part to the priest and his magical formulas; and out of the confusion of symbol with priest grew mythology, which personalized the symbol into an anthropomorphic deity, and heard in the ritualistic formula the voice of the "god." These gods still carried with them the old animal and plant symbols, as a rule. Zeus had his eagle, Minerva her owl, Hengist (Old German for "stallion") his horse. But mythology steadily became an anthropomorphic religion which interpreted nature wholly in terms of the human economy. The cosmos was a divine kingdom, ruled by a divine governor and his court. Metaphor was reversed, nature being interpreted in terms of human relations.

The large religious myth, often congregating a whole pantheon of local deities, supported the advance to large civilized economy. It defined political boundaries, supported new political programs, brought neighboring tribes into a more closely integrated national or imperial economy, provided the vehicle of transmittal for cultural adaptation. The scholar today, reconstructing this evolution of religious myth, finds there a significant quality and tension. There was usually a dominant myth, which used the symbolism of large cosmic design, that of sun and moon and the annual cycle of the constellations, to indicate the absolute and eternal status of some reigning political-economic system. But there was also a recessive or submerged myth, closer to primitivism in its animal and plant imagery, and more concerned with the process of regeneration which perpetuates all living things. This more humble, popular myth often arose to displace the dominant myth, expanding in its turn to cosmic dimensions, and replacing the Sun of Heaven, Lord of Lords and King of Kings, by the Divine Father and Mother of the universe; or it envisioned the eternal cosmic generation of a Holy Family, manifest in all earthly regeneration in humble and ephemeral copies. The recessive myth was strong in its perception of the *domestic* origin of all social adaptation; and it could topple dynasties and destroy empires supported upon olympian religion, which put form before content, and prized law and order more than life itself.

However, it is apparent that social adaptation, extending domestic adaptation to an ever larger socialized group, must forever move between two poles in its evolution of social pattern. Its origin lies in individual variations of development and acquired character, induced by parental love in the domestic interior or home. The extent of the social spread of new adaptive type, however, depends upon the nature of the material into which it spreads. Retrospectively viewed, the evolution of primitive and civilized myth must be seen as a more or less deliberate or sustained effort of the group to control the spread of new adaptive type, suppressing this type and sanctifying that type. Custom became explicit law. Clearly, what is truly adaptive depends not upon chance, but upon the natures of things. It depends, first, upon the nature of life with its permanent conditions; secondly, upon the nature of the habitat to which life must be adjusted. The group economy, with its internal and external adaptation, is conditioned in its persistence by "natural law," which is nothing more nor less than the dependence of *all* persistence of group and type upon reciprocal adaptations among things. Primitive myth thus appears as an effort to establish the clan economy upon a conception of the natural ecology of plants and animals. In nature, reciprocal adaptation preserves a plurality of species. So might a plurality of clans be preserved, if each will be "true to itself," i.e. preserve its internal economy; and we have the imagery which identifies each clan with some plant or animal type. This perception of the symbiotic economy of plant and animal species then supported the advance to a clan-system or primitive nation. The other pole of social adaptation lies outside the group, external to man, in "nature." The civilized myth looked beyond living nature to cosmic nature or the "universe." It conceived of a natural economy manifest in the periodicity of "celestial" motions, those of the sun, moon, and stars. These motions evidently support the persistence of all type. They determine the regular seasons, which condition all plant and animal growth. *The human economy is interlocked with the economy of nature.* The persistence, prosperity, and increase of human society is dependent upon its conformity to "natural law." The religious myth therefore attempted to establish the social economy upon a conception of natural economy framed in such terms as would indicate the relationship between human and natural economy, i.e. the relationship of man to nature. The myth used anthropomorphic imagery, seeing in the cosmos an eternal kingdom or a divine family; but it steadily worked to direct attention upon natural occurrence itself, in that its intention was to adjust custom and law to external conditions in improved human adaptation to nature. Myth inevitably moved toward *science,* which makes imagery and vocabulary, whatever its anthropomorphic origin, the tool of objective description. The advance to science was bridged by monotheistic religion, which appreciated the unity of cosmos and "natural law," and conceived of God as cosmic law or lawgiver.

This advance was made in the great river-basin civilizations of Egypt and Mesopotamia, where great empires arose dependent for their persistence only upon their internal adaptation; but it is almost wholly through the Greek people that the advance was channeled to the modern world.

To appreciate properly this cultural inheritance which comes to us from Greece, we must know, first, that Greek science, and also the modern science which later recovered the Greek insight, were still myth, only in less degree anthropomorphic than the religions which they displaced. The basic postulate of "natural law" is anthropomorphic fiction, projecting the design of human institutions into nature at large. There *is* law in nature; but it is not the "law" envisaged either by Greek or by modern science. Secondly, we must understand the character and history of the Greek people, which gave them such disproportionate influence over the further evolution of civilization.

The Greek people were descendants of primitive societies which had migrated from the north into the rich Mediterranean civilization. These societies were evidently of a very high primitive type, intensely cultured; and they tried to preserve this cultural integrity in their new surroundings. They established small "cities," economically self-sufficient and fiercely independent; for they were unwilling to exchange their high primitive culture for the decadent culture of the large civilization they had entered. Thus, they attempted to establish a new form of social adaptation, taking much from civilized culture but retaining the virtues of primitivism. Their effort failed; but it nevertheless helped to make apparent, for all time, the structure and conditions of social economy. Primitive man owed his increase to the adaptations which made of the group a closely knit, amicable society, composed of individuals bound by fraternal habit. Civilization proposes to enlarge society; but it is always in danger of losing, and periodically does lose, the associative adaptation upon which its persistence depends.

A civilized society, it might seem, should last forever. What could destroy a group possessed of such variety of genic and acquired character, so adaptable, and possessed of such control over its economic resources? The civilizations which arose in the large river-valleys believed themselves to be eternal. They forgot their humble origins in primitive society, they deified themselves and their dynasties, they confused their social structure with that of cosmos itself. Nor were they ever literally and bodily wiped out. Yet those early civilizations reverted, one and all, to a caricature of primitivism. For a thousand years they prospered and increased; for another thousand or more they declined and staved off collapse; but finally they fell victim to an incurable disease. The great temples and palaces crumbled, the monuments gathered sand, the vast irrigation projects fell into disrepair, the bureaucracies lost their skills, the captains and the kings departed; and the small herdsman and cultivator inherited the earth. What destroys civilization? What ennui enervates it? What paralysis lames it? What malady runs in its veins and infects its genes?

Those great civilizations died from within; they decayed for lack of social adaptation, internal to the group. Not until they were dry-rotted from within did they become loot for "barbarian," more primitive neighbors. Their associative adaptation hardened and atrophied, their culture crystallized, their *basic* economy decayed; and, as it did so, irrigation and storage were neglected, and education became verbal mimicry. There arose local loyalties, binding local groups; and the great society became a dead shell, housing a score or hundred small populations, only nominally united.

Those decadent civilizations neglected the family, and with it the fraternal habit that had made of an animal population a human society. They deified the State, personified in the Great King. They made their King a god, and their God a king. *They would not know that God is only and always a child, not in the skies but in the human family.* They set high their dynasties; they were abject before their governing groups, which became breeding populations jealously retaining within themselves their genic and acquired character, and living in economic parasitism upon the people at large. As the governing group lost the virtue which had given it leadership, it bolstered itself by harsh enforcement of law and authority, with military discipline sanctified by orthodox religion. But nothing helped, because this deification of the State cut the living bond which unifies society, and destroyed the channel through which the affections bred in the home must flow into the body corporate of society. Always, always there appeared this governing élite with its attendant priesthood, this class which identified its order with the State and its "mind" with God. It was a class set apart and aloof, like a scab, a clan which inbred and deteriorated, which mistook pride of family for affection and loyalty, and which finally became the cancer which destroyed society. Not once, but always, civilized society was destroyed by it royal and priestly rulers. Sooner or later the real forces of society, those developed in the home, ate through and undermined and tumbled down those parasitic classes. Yet what was the error of those civilizations? Must not a society have leadership? It must. Their error was to believe that human character is *genically* transmitted, and that virtue is guaranteed by bodily descent. The founders of those dynasties and ruling groups were men of virtue and power, bringing to the large society a genuine affection and care; but, preoccupied with state affairs, they left the upbringing of their progeny to courtiers or slaves; and each new generation transmitted less than it received of social wisdom.

The Greeks were critical of the decadent civilizations into which they had come. They strove to prevent the division of society into governing and governed classes. They tolerated no powerful priesthoods. They tried to perpetuate in their political institutions the habit of the small primitive group. They sent their surplus populations to colonize new cities, often distant from the mother city. They tended to equate justice with *freedom*, which is the power of the individual to participate in social evolution, and to secure in this way the diversity of habit which makes for adaptability. But the forces which impel civilized society were as effective then as now. Their effort availed only to throw the Greeks at last into ruinous intercivic war, leaving them subject to imperial Macedon. But out of their struggle came the ideal of liberty, supported by the myth of "natural law," one of the two great antique myths which were to direct the progress to modern civilization.

The Greeks did not originate the concept of cosmic law; but they purified it of its mythological elements, which had confused cosmic law with a cosmic lawgiver. Seeing in society a system of economy bound by "impersonal," i.e. superpersonal, custom, they imagined a natural economy persisting in virtue of impersonal natural law. They moved, in short, from individual to social anthropomorphism. They projected not God, but the City of God, into the sky. They believed themselves, however—and the belief is evidence of their intention—to have left behind all anthropomorphic fiction, and to have established a purely objective truth. Natural law is no myth, their thinkers insisted. It is literal and sober truth, everywhere manifest to the human *reason*. We are so much the children of this Greek myth that even where we verbally deny it, we still in our thoughts affirm and pursue it, confusing natural science with faith in natural law. Just what was that "reason" extolled by the Greek thinker? It was nothing else than the claim to knowledge of the eternal cosmic *structure* which maintains all natural economy and allows "nature," everywhere transient in its particular occurrence, to persist in time. Modern criticism has exploded this fiction of an eternal "natural law" intuited by an infallible reason. But the Greek myth, because of its intention to make natural science the director and preserver of the human economy, intelligently adjusting this economy to the larger economy of nature, firmly established *the human intellect.* Let us call this rationalistic myth, mother of science but falling short of science, "philosophy"!

From antiquity, the civilization progenitor to our own, came down a second religious myth. This was Christianity, which stayed closer to the recessive type of myth in its domestic and biological symbolism. For Christianity, God was still Father and King, personal Redeemer of the world, Lamb whose blood washed nature clean, Vine of whom we are the branches. But in Christianity the older myth of a living and regenerate nature was tied to a cosmic myth which saw *nature* as *a temporal creation.* Where the Greek tradition focused thought upon eternal form, the Christian tradition was historically oriented, and focused thought upon *structural change.* It spoke of that which transcends, abrogates, and reshapes all custom and law. The Christian myth was a parable antithetical but complementary to the Greek myth of natural law. Out of the interplay between these two parables, each critical of the other, was generated the critical faith which is contemporary science.

There is eternal law, cosmic structure, persisting through all natural occurrence and maintaining itself in the largest as in the most minute design of nature! No, there is that which transcends law, stales all custom, and creates nature and structure at once! The Greek and Christian myths were dovetailed into *theology,* which taught that God continually creates nature in the form of his eternal thought, known to reason as natural law. This theological self-contradiction did not make sense; nor did the theologian pretend otherwise. Faith is divinely revealed truth, he said; and it consequently transcends reason. The reason takes us to natural law, faith takes us to the Creator of law. The virtue of theology was its determination to preserve both myths, relinquishing neither insight. It challenged the thinker to think the unthinkable; and this the thinker finally proceeded to do. Should not man, empowered by faith to identify his will with that of God, participate in the divine work of creation? Should not a redeemed society be about its Father's business, and also create law, reforming law in the strength of moral insight? A *science* illumined by faith *must go beyond reason,* seeing as God sees, taught Roger Bacon and his successors.

There arose a reformed church which placed religious responsibility in the congregation of believers, a reformed science which made observed particular fact its criterion of truth, and a reformed society which transferred the divine right of the King to a people ready for moral and religious responsibility. The Greek philosopher had exhorted the rational man to become in his private behavior a citizen of the City of God, ruled by natural and divine law; but he had not expected, as a rule, to establish this City on earth. The combination of Greek philosophy with Christian creationism did encourage this expectation. The Christian church had identified itself as this divine City; and the reformed congregations went further, requiring that society *in its entirety* should religiously rule itself, and secure the political power needed to do this. Out of religious, scientific, and political reformation issued *modern society,* which by "the law of Nature and of Nature's God" placed moral responsibility and political power inalienably in the individual, and used legislation, creating new law, as the instrument of indefinite social progress.

In this way, the marriage of Greek and Christian myth had issue in a new and startling conception of natural law. *Natural law is that necessity which requires of each in-*

dividual his due participation in legislation securing social progress. This law looks to no fixed social structure, reflecting that of eternity. It looks to the continued progressive reform of social structure. Yet it still conceives this social progress to be the pursuit and progressive realization of eternal justice. It still looks to an absolute moral distinction between good and evil, enabling society to distinguish between social progress and social disintegration and decay. What is this eternal, absolute *moral* law, that underpins the universe yet requires the fluidity of all natural law and structure? Will modern science inform modern man of that universal moral necessity, to adjust himself to which man must keep eternally on the run, reforming his social structure from day to day by progressive legislation?

Philosophy had professed to give man a natural knowledge which was also moral wisdom. The universe is a great economy, it taught, composed of species each of which has its cosmic place and specific function. Man is a species whose specific distinction is reason, giving intelligence of the natural economy and man's place in it. Very well, we are specifically human, rational, intelligent! Just what is our place and function in this cosmos, our duty toward it, our responsibility in it? Man's duty is to be rational, reasonable, intelligent! Yes, but precisely what do reason and intelligence require? They require us to be reasonable and intelligent! Intelligent of what? Intelligent of your intelligence! Is this an answer to the question: What must we do to be saved?

Modern science rightly rejected Greek rationalism. Man has no rational intuition of cosmic economy and universal structure, it announced; but he may by observation and hypothesis come progressively closer to knowledge of that structure. Very well, he comes closer to it. He progresses from Newtonian to Einsteinian mechanics, and from this to quantum mechanics. The true structure is always just ahead. And so it is with the progressive reform of social structure! Just experiment further, legislate, reform this and that! The social structure will progressively approach what ought to be. But how shall we know when we have bettered things, and not merely marred them? What is the better society, and what the worse? Is it certain that men need only legislate in concert in order to legislate justly? Is there no concerted error, is there never concert of evil? Merely by knowing that we ought to vote, do we know how to vote, what to vote for?

Neither philosophy nor modern science gave man knowledge of moral law. Both assured man of his intelligence of the moral economy of nature; but neither philosophy nor modern science documented this statement, by describing the cosmic economy and showing man his place in it. *Modern criticism* arose to make clear the fatuity, at once scientific and moral, of philosophy. Of what value is that philosophy, asked the critic, which fixates itself on types and never inquires into the particular causes of occurrence? Modern science did make such inquiry, and, seeking, found. But it still bolstered itself upon the fiction of a universal structure, a ubiquitous, universal, and complex type, to which particular occurrence must still and always defer. So the modern critic turned his attack upon modern science. How should *particular* occurrence, Hume asked two centuries ago, be universally *necessitated?* If the event is particularly caused, how should it be universally caused? No, Hume wrote, one finds in particular occurrence no necessity of any sort, however hard or closely one looks. That supposed structure necessitating events must be subjective illusion. It is just the mind's projection into nature of its own mental structure or habit. Hume was not far wrong, historically speaking. The notion of universal structure was in truth an anthropomorphic metaphor, by which man read into nature not his mental structure but that of his society with its fixed law. However, the notion of natural structure is not invalidated by its historical origin, if it be scientifically confirmed; and science does discover in nature plenty of structure, and discovers much structure that is most persistent and enduring.

But Hume's criticism went deeper than his explicit doctrine. This is why it threw the modern intellect into a tailspin from which it has not yet emerged, and from which, it sometimes seems, it prefers not to emerge. The motive of Hume's criticism was moral, not narrowly scientific. What Hume struck down, effectively enough, was the fallacy of a natural structure which holds nature in an eternal straitjacket. Our true science of society, he taught, is an historical science, one which shows that, and how, and why, society has created its own law and thereby continually reshaped its own structure. He was skeptical only of a purely theoretical science, fixated still upon the dogma of a universal and absolute necessity imposed upon all particular occurence.

Hume was justified in the nineteenth century by the rise of evolutionary science, which informs us that all natural structure is *adaptive type,* persisting as a form of reciprocal adaptation among the particular existents which compose a world in radical change. There has been an evolution or natural progress of adaptive type, supporting the progressive creation of the natural economy. "Modern science" was not quite modern! It was still Greek myth in its adherence to the dogma of necessary structure, eternally beckoning on the pursuant theorist. Is evolutionary science at last the straight truth, freed from myth? If it is, it must provide that moral wisdom which discloses the natural economy and man's place in it. It must reveal to us the moral law which lies deeper than structure, determining what structure may persist and what not, the rise and decline of structures disclosing the creation of the world. Science must make man intelligent not only of his own intelligence, but of all that is, not only in its type or structure, but in its coming to be, its passing away, its right to persist.

* 6 *

THE PLACE OF MAN IN

THE PHYSICAL COSMOS

QUITE properly, man attempted to place his human life in a cosmic context; and, quite rightly, he discovered in that largest context a *physical* structure, supporting a physical world. Inevitably, he learned not to attribute to physical nature the properties of living nature and the designs of human nature. He rid himself of every anthropomorphic fantasy, to find in physical nature, that which extends to the confines of space and which even defines the form of space, an actuality which seems quite disparate from life, incommensurable with life, unrelated to life, careless of life.

Yet, out of that physical matter grew or came life! In one place at least, on the surface of this earth, there grew out of chemical matter the living economy. The evolution of life is like the growth of a plant, growing out of the flowerpot which is the physical cosmos. The flower of the plant is man with his mind and his intellect, his art and his science and his religion. The roots of the plant are the bacteria of the soil, the activities of which support vegetation, which then supports animal and human life. Why and how did this evolution of life proceed out of inorganic nature? Is that not mysterious, inexplicable? Well, why and how does a plant grow in its flowerpot? Is evolution more mysterious than the growth of an organism? Both are facts, to be accepted. But no, the plant grows from a seed, something organic and living. Evolution proceeded out of inorganic matter, by definition not organic and living!

The development of modern physics destroyed all earlier conception, progressively discovered to be fallacious and wishful fantasy, of continuity between life and the physical cosmos. Life came to be seen as an inconsiderable and inexplicable accident, peculiar to this planet, which physical science found to be a minute speck moving in an almost, but not quite, infinite space. No science or philosophy which leaves life so insignificant in this universe is worth the paper it is written on; but evolutionary biology goes far toward providing us with scientific wisdom. Given the origin of life, it can explain the evolution of life. That original life became vegetable and animal life. It became mammalian life and primitive humanity, all in virtue of the group adaptation which is the ground floor of living matter. The primitive society became the civilized society, which grows its own food, and comes to replace the natural ecology of organic nature with the humanly controlled economy of crops and herds. This whole *organic* evolution is explicable as the work of a single associated group, the evolution being directed at every moment by the *individual variants* which *reproduced their variation in adaptive type*. Here is much that is awe-inspiring, but nothing that is mysterious in the sense of being causally inexplicable. If there is mystery, it is the individuation of nature, which seems to be just ineluctable particular necessity.

This organic science is moral science. It is good to live. Each living organism bears an inalienable, intrinsic value, in and for and to itself. Good, therefore, is any numerical increase of life. Population increase means value increase. But population increase is conditioned by reciprocal adaptation of all types. Only individuals exist, and the existence of each individual is due to and conditioned by the adaptations among individuals, especially those of individuals to their groups. Thus, derivatively good, as auxiliary to living increase, is all adaptive character conditioning increase. Each individual has a secondary value, not intrinsic but extrinsic. It is better or worse according as it contributes to the organic economy; and *best* are those individual variants which originate adaptive type conditioning living increase. *These individuals created the organic economy.* Best is the creative character which modifies adaptive structure, widening the basis of the economy. Evolutionary science is moral wisdom because it is religious truth, telling us of the causes of life's creation. These causes do not lie in heaven. They work within the organic economy itself, and are the individual variants which here create and there destroy life. To convert descriptive biology into moral wisdom and religious truth, it is necessary only to affirm the intrinsic goodness of life, the value of life to the organism which lives. All else follows.

But the modern intellect is not able to accept from science this moral wisdom and religious truth, because it believes that life, with its evolution, is an accident in the world, a local and ephemeral phenomenon manifesting in a peculiar way the eternal necessities of physical structure. Whatever happens is physically necessitated; and even if we allow that there has been an evolution of physical matter, conditioned by individual variations of molecules or atoms or what not, we cannot ascribe to these physical variants any intrinsic value, nor consequently any derivative extrinsic value. Man's evaluation of life as good is just an understandable selfishness. Life is finally just the proclivity of molecules and atoms to be what they are, impelled upon their individual paths, and resisting by their *inertia* any deflection from that path. Life, in short, is a peculiar type of inertia, an absence of life. It is impossible, scientifically, to prefer life to death, to prefer what is adaptive type to what is not, to place any scientific value upon anything. Of course, science itself has and is value; but the value of science is finally man's evaluation of his intelligent life, which is good only because it is his specific type of inertia and death.

Physical science, which was advanced by those who desired to support human morality upon the discovery of the moral economy of cosmic nature, became in modern science the great demoralizer. *Four centuries of modern science have deprived man of all moral and religious faith.* We are moral or religious in spite of our science. Intellect is of the head only, in no degree of the heart; and by our science we are destroyed, for science places power in the hands of those who have committed themselves most irrevocably to an immoral and irreligious faith. How should there be morality and religion in a science which denies the actualities of creation and the significance of organic evolution and human progress, and which tells us that nature is in truth a study in black and white, the values of nature, religious and aesthetic and moral, being painted in by ourselves. What shall we do with a science which reduces psychological, biological, chemical, and every other structure to a structure which is that of an energy everywhere essentially the same? Physical science, indeed, has a perverse morality of its own. Energy is by definition irreducible, indestructible, always quantitatively the same. There is absolute conservation of energy. The whole actuality of things is these energies. Nothing can ever really be gained, nor can anything be really lost. All that occurs is a redistribution of the real in space.

If we could forget physics, biology would provide moral and religious science. We ourselves are that adaptable group

which established life on earth. We are the group in which
originated the variations which established new associative
type preserving and amplifying the life on this planet. We
created and continually redeemed this terrestrial life, in virtue of the association or community which preserved these
individual variations in group type. We, and no celestial fiction, are the god of life, which is our handiwork. It is explicable that we today should take the organic economy intelligently in hand, creating new specific type as we can and
will. Let us prize only what is "specifically" human, and we
will prize and cultivate those plant and animal populations
which condition our persistence. *In increasing our own
population, we increase the living population* on this earth.
Evolutionary biology has a quantitative measure of value
in the population of this earth; it has a qualitative criterion
of value in the adaptation which conditions living persistence; and it provides a science of value in the knowledge
of what has conditioned living increase in the past. Here is
a moral and religious science of the creation of life. The
fertile organism is worth more than the sterile, the individual variant which originates better adaptive type is
worth more than the stereotyped which stays within its type;
and most valuable of all is the human individual whose
variation conditions human increase, the support of which
and consequence of which is living increase. It is not true
that man takes all and gives nothing in return. For his joy
of creation he pays in the amplification of life; and man, in
exploiting his natural resources, pays in the consequent increase of the terrestrial living population. But all this science with its values dissipates in dust, if life is worth no
more than dust. What would give life cosmic value?

Religion would tell us that truly good, best of all, absolute and eternal good, is the activity of creation itself. The
material of the world is the product of past creation and the

condition of present creation, so that its value is indicative and derivative. Creation is fierce and terrible joy, of which what we call pleasure is the remote and faint echo, comfortable physiological reminiscence of the joys which shook, thrilled, deified, and made incandescent our near or remote ancestors. It is this knowledge of creation which modern science, suppressing the creation myth which gave it birth and power, has invalidated. We may not see even in the creation of terrestrial life anything else than physical inertia. The religions which taught creative joy are discarded as mere myth, void of insight and of truth.

It is necessary, of course, that the vehicles of creative joy should be discarded when they have served their time. The word of Christ, individual variant whose establishment was Christian civilization, cannot indefinitely preserve his creation. The Christian insight must be recovered, and restated in new gospel truth. The demoralization of western man began in religious orthodoxy itself. It was the Christian Fathers who taught that the new wine poured by Jesus of Nazareth could be contained in the old bottles of Greek philosophy, unconsciously but nevertheless stupidly thereby denying the creative and therefore unparalleled act of Christ himself. From them flows all of this modern amoralism! They denied Christ Creator, thinking to do him homage by calling him repetition and true copy of God Creator. There appears a new and unparalleled thing, bringing other things into new community; but there always appear those things which will crystallize the new type, denying the individuality of its source, confusing the source with themselves which bear the type. So, said the Christian Fathers, we and the holy Church are Christ. Dear Christ, that you should be so blasphemed, and be made the perverter of truth, founder of a church which exists to insulate the individual from you, your profound disturbance, and your inexhaustible truth! Let it be known that Christ died on Calvary, and that he exists in no one, but is eternally what he was; and let those who love Christ not pretend to the character, power, and authority of Christ! What character, authority, and power we possess are our own. Power has its measure and its validation in what it effects, not in its past causes.

The Christian, Jewish, and Arab theologians were idolaters who turned the adoration of creative act, truly God if God there be, into pagan philosophy which taught that all occurrence manifests eternal form, so that there is no true creation. That theologized philosophy became modern theoretical science. The writer of the fourth gospel began this perversity, when he wrote that in the beginning was the *Word,* i.e. the logos or eternal form, and that this Word was made flesh and dwelt among us. The theologians then quite brazenly converted Christian truth into pagan philosophy, which explicitly denied creation. Modern science had only to relinquish the pharisaical theology in order to identify the eternal structure which is the word or thought of God with the eternal infinity of physically structured space, definable in terms of some universal theory ostensibly comprehensive of last things. The modern intellect confined itself to the pursuit of this theory, approximately grasped and probably known in every theoretical hypothesis.

Modern science limits creation to the provision of particular difference, which invests all particular manifestations of eternal structure. This is to limit creation to the perpetuation only of what is formless and chaotic in the world, and to attribute all form to eternal necessity; and because the value of particular character can be known only through its establishment of form, this is to deny all value to particular character, intrinsically and as such. Nor can the theorist allow value to specific, generic, or any other form, since the origin of this is also that eternal and universal structure which of necessity appears in everything.

The transition from medieval theology to modern theoretical science is most clearly seen in the thought of Descartes, who is often called, unfortunately with only too much truth, "the founder of modern philosophy." God created matter and man, each in its own form, said Descartes. This was his parting genuflection to theology. God created all motion in *geometrical* form; and he created man in *rational* form, cognizant of geometry. However, he allowed to man the freedom of will either to be cognizant and human, or to revert to material, geometrical form. Thus Descartes reduced all morality and religion to the duty to pursue and apply physical science, which understands all material motion as geometrically structured. Cease from impious and useless inquiry into the inscrutable natures of things, advised Descartes. The nature of things is to be geometrical. Be truly religious by cultivating and applying your God-given reason, informing you of physical structure. Exploit matter to the full—that is the true service of God! Reason is for use, not for speculation into the relationship of matter and mind, and other mysteries of the inscrutable will of God. Take what belongs within reason, forget what lies beyond reason!

In this way Descartes deflected the impetus of medieval piety into the pursuit and use of physical science. It was quickly seen that Descartes's theology was only window dressing. One does not need a creator, to envisage matter and mind as *eternal* structures, necessarily manifest. The only puzzle left by the Cartesian philosophy was that there should be two functions of eternal structure, one in the matter moved, and the other in the cognizant mind. But let us see that theology always was irreligion, which hypocritically admits the creation of the world by God only at once to deny to God any subsequent place in the world. Theology is always orthodoxy, denying the creative act where it works and moves. It has always said, Lord! Lord! to an idol, crucifying the Creator.

Theoretical science makes nature wholly servant unto man, giving him knowledge of the necessities under which nature moves, and giving him thereby power to interfere in these motions, deflecting them as he will to his own service. Roger Bacon in the thirteenth century pleaded with the Church to avail itself of this new science, which otherwise would become the instrument of the enemies of the Church. The Church refused this gift, imprisoning and burning its would-be benefactors. So Descartes protestantly brings the gift to society at large. Use this science to abolish poverty, vice, and crime, he says. Establish your economy upon it, make it your government! Let the Enlightenment shine! The Age of Reason is come!

And how should this new power be used, which provides every means? To what ends shall it be directed? For Descartes and the modern world which followed him, it seemed enough to use the power, to insure its being used aright. Because the advance of science is a progress, it seemed that the increasing use of science must be the whole of progress. But what sort of science was this, which advised us that the fullest exploitation of matter to *any* end is the whole duty of man? What sort of God would deliver matter so irrevocably into the hands of his creature man, requiring only that man most largely exploit matter to his use? Shall man bring no service in his turn to the matter which sustains him? Shall the great law of nature which makes *reciprocal* adaptation the condition of persistence be now annulled? Was it a fair and just God which made the living bodies of plants, the mobile and sensitive bodies of animals, the minded and delicate bodies of men and women and children merely the matter which the biologist or the psychologist shall unscrupulously exploit? Who shall do this exploiting, in whose interest, to what end? Where were you, Francis of Assisi, you who found brothers and sisters in the birds and the flowers, when this perverse and idolatrous doctrine possessed itself of the modern mind?

What is the alternative to the Cartesian denial of life creative and beneficent? It is to learn of the continuity of the evolution of matter, which was physical, then chemical, finally organic and human. The *physical* world flowers in life, as the organic world flowers in man. There is that in physical matter which conditioned the evolution of life. The physical cosmos is an *economy,* and living nature is an important part and parcel of that larger economy. Life was conditioned in its whole evolution by the physical cosmos. The true law of nature, requiring reciprocal adaptation in all that persists, goes back to the beginning of the world. It always was effective; and it determined, and always will remain to determine, the ground floor of nature.

Philosophers since Descartes, not perceiving that their error was their unbridgeable dualism of *life* and physical nature, have wasted their energies upon "the dualism of mind and matter." The idealist philosopher has taught that physical structure is "really" the structure of mind in its physical appearance, the human mind being a molecule in the great ocean of "Mind" which is the universe, everywhere identical in this *structure*. The materialist philosopher says exactly the same nonsense, only he insists that the structure be called "matter," not "Mind." Neither philosophy has any scientific nor moral significance. Both exist only to evade the real issue, which is why nature exhibits and maintains these plural structures, specifically different whatever their "universal" similarity. More intelligible and more intelligent is the skeptical philosophy which holds this relationship between "matter" and "mind" to be inscrutable, our minds imposing upon nature a mental structure which need not be, and probably is not, that of nature external to man. This at least leaves open the question why nature is there chemically structured, and here organically structured, and at last socially structured.

But we have come to the place where science and logic make clear the fatuities of the philosophers, and where the course of human events makes moral wisdom, instructing how science should be used, the condition of peace and human persistence. There are only two alternatives open to us. One is to revert to myth. We can resort to the old myths, return authority to priests and rabbis, defer to "theology which transcends reason," undertake moral rearmament by force of will without moral insight, drool over the order and piety of medieval feudalism, civil and clerical; we can concoct new myths of a barbaric and Nietzschean sort, glorify myth as a form of intuition superior to intellect, raise "art" above science. Or we can grapple scientifically with this problem of the place of man in the moral economy of nature, knowing that the key to the problem lies in the evolution from physical structure to social structure through the intermediary of organic structure.

Evolutionary science indicates what sort of process continuously creates living nature. The organisms living today are creatures of those that lived yesterday and creators of those that live tomorrow. Living organisms were always reciprocally adapted, responding to one another in adaptive ways. This specific response indicates a sensitivity of some sort to different types of external stimulus. This constitutive reciprocity has supported the evolution from the bacteria to man, where it appears as the intelligence which is common sense and scientific discernment of types of stimulus. Evolutionary biology assures us of the moral economy of life, and of the service man brings to living nature in return for the use of its organic resources. It provides both the criteria and the data of a science of ethics, completely empirical in its use of the postulates of science. But it is also necessary to know that this preference of the living to the nonliving, i.e. of life over death, is not just egoistic vanity. *We must know that the center line of organic evolution stretches back to the beginning of the world,* and that it delineates the succession of new adaptive forms which have sustained and amplified the creation of the physical cosmos, i.e. of matter. We must find in the physical and chemical structure described by physicochemical theory the product of the creative evolution of physicochemical type, conditioning and conditioned by the progressive increase of matter. We must know that the material increase of man is the condition of the material increase of terrestrial life, and that this increase today conditions the increase of universal matter and the further creation of cosmos.

* 7 *

THE EVOLUTION OR

CREATION OF MATTER

IT is generally conceded today that matter is destructible. Atoms may disintegrate or come into being; one sort of atom may become another sort, the atoms undergoing change of chemical constitution. It is agreed that there has been evolution of material and chemical structure. But clear thinking and sustained inquiry are hindered by old dogma and ingrained habits of thought. The old dogma of the indestructibility of matter reappears in the new dogma of the necessary and absolute conservation of energy in nature. Supporting these dogmas is the ancient confusion which has fathered every dogma. This is *the confusion of substance* or being, real and therefore individuated, *with type,* which is *our perception of similarity* among individual things and particular occurrences. Type is not individual, and strictly speaking not real, except as an idea in our minds. The similarities indicated by types are real similarities; but the types themselves are not properties of things, but statistical averages. Things similar in a certain respect are of a certain type. Material things are those which have mass, and exert similar gravitational force.

The old "matter" was a confusion of atoms, real individual things no two of which are identical, with mental type or self-identical idea. Variant atoms may be of identical type, say hydrogen type. It is now seen that atoms may change in properties and type, one sort of atom becoming another sort. Atoms may radically change in their properties and reactions. This means that atomic type is not immutable, that atoms may become similar or cease to be similar. There has presumably been an evolution of atomic type. But the old confusion with its eternalistic dogma is now retained in the concept of "energy." The change of type, it is supposed, is not a change of substance. The substance which changes is "energy," and "energy" remains identical in quantity and basic structure under every change of superficial atomic form. If we allow that the physical world changes in its basic structure, defined by the formulas which define "energy," how shall we explain the causal reactions responsible for change of atomic type? Let us say, rather, that physical things are ultimately composed of minute entities identical and immutable in type, for example energy-waves or quanta, and that all qualitative change of type is only a change in the spatial distribution of these minute entities. This means that all change of substance, property, or quality is mental illusion, the only real change being that of spatial relationship. The sole reality is change of spatio-temporal position. In this case, the evolution of matter, i.e. of atomic and other type, is only a succession of types of spatio-temporal relationship, and not one of real substances and properties, so that it is of little significance.

Yet the evolution of life, i.e. of organic type, is only a further extension of the evolution of chemical type. All evolution, it follows, is inconsequential. Given the initial distribution of the minute, immutable, eternal entities which compose physical nature, the whole evolution may be described as the result of physical necessity, appearing in the "laws" of material evolution. The sole authentic knowledge is physical theory, defining the eternal structure of "energy." There is neither need nor possibility of applying here such concepts as adaptation, selection, individual variation. Physics and chemistry may invade biology; but there can be no invasion of physical science by biologists. Some day there will be but one science, explaining all particular occurrence as a manifestation of physical necessity, working upon some initial distribution of energy to produce all past "evolution of type."

What sort of science would be an evolutionary physics, explaining the evolution of physical, chemical, and mineral type as the result of "natural selection" working upon "individual variations"? This science would explain the creation of the cosmos as proceeding from something original, but as yet unstructured, to a first adaptive type, and thence to the continual modification of that first type in a succession of adaptive types. This creation would have started at some point in space-time, the definition of space-time becoming possible in terms of the physical types so established. The chaos, void of type, out of which formed matter arose, would of necessity remain indefinable. There would be continual increase and spread of physically structured matter, this increase being conditioned by, and again conditioning, the continual creation of new adaptive type. Physical constants—the speed of light, e, the quantum, etc. —would be accepted as indices of a most ubiquitous, even universal, uniformity of type, presumably that which appeared first and was modified in all later adaptation.

Is this conceivable? Yes, the hypothesis is intelligible and reasonable enough. If there is evolution of adaptive type in the macroscopic organic realm, there may be evolution of adaptive type in the microscopic physical realm. Indeed, the first requires the second. Molecules in the organism do not behave as do "the same molecules" in crystals, because they react to a different context. In man, molecular change may condition thought process. But, if molecules can be described only with respect to particular or typical situations, so can atoms, electrons, quanta.

However, if we can describe each and every physical occurrence (and whatever happens is physical occurrence) as the particular variant of a universal, immutable structure, appearing unchanged in its every manifestation, should we bother about changes of physical, chemical, or other type? Why be concerned whether energy appears in this or that type, chemical, organic, or human? Why use many types, if the single type which we call "physical structure" best supports description and prediction? First, because we are most interested in change of type. It makes a difference whether we are humanly alive or chemical dust. We would not want to change the mineral types of the earth's surface in such a way as to destroy living type. We would not want to start a chain reaction which would leave no free oxygen in the atmosphere. Secondly, we should reject the notion of "physical necessity," except as a shorthand expression for particular necessities which everywhere differ not only as to type, but particularly. Thirdly, we are interested in the creation of the cosmos, i.e. of physical, chemical, organic, animal, and human type. The power to predict is not the sole nor the chief power of man. More important is the power to act, deflecting the course of events, and assuring *or preventing* that which is predictable in terms of past occurrence and "physical necessity." *Man is not a type!* He is creative of type, even of physical type.

The study of organic evolution informs us that evolutionary change of type is due to the individual variations of units associated in groups, and conditioned by material increase in number and mass of groups, causing congestion.

Congestion due to increase is the occasion of all group re-adaptation and change of type. If there has been a creation of the physical world, with continual increase of formed matter, the evolution of material type should similarly follow from congestion, and be an evolution of adaptive type. Why are there rare and abundant minerals, and rare and abundant elements (atomic types), unless it be that some chemical types are better adapted to their local conditions? There is evidently persistence, extinction, and readaptive change of physical type. The evolution of living species is a clue to the evolution of all material type.

We know that the existence of organisms and the persistence of groups require so much space, light, air, water, mineral and organic sustenance. A living population can be poisoned by its own metabolic by-products, or by its own dead. It can be choked by becoming too densely packed. *There is for every type of group adaptation an optimum distribution-density.* If the group is too scattered, association and gene exchange are affected. If it is too dense, congestion occurs. The evolution of adaptive type has bettered this optimum distribution, and allowed further increase within the same habitat. The new group readaptation then conditions the establishment of novel types of external adaptation. Of course, the most immediate relief from congestion is obtained by mobility, allowing wider spatial distribution. However, expansion destroys the old association, the group becoming a phylad of cognate groups. This is why the quantitative evolution of living matter is a qualitative evolution of species, genera, etc. New adaptation of any sort, if it conditions increase, at once begins to work selectively, favoring the establishment of types better able to survive under congested conditions.

We are most familiar with this evolutionary process in human progress. The domestication and cultivation of ani-

mals and plants occasioned great human increase, conditioning the evolution of new institutionalized group habits. It
led to the urbanization of part of the population, the urban
population then proceeding to a far-reaching evolution of
domestic and social habit. The domestication of animals
and plants was an epochal event, reversing the largest direction of organic evolution. This had been radiant or
dispersive, being a continual multiplication of groups
conditioning the continual radiation of new divergent
type. Evolution now became convergent, gathering mankind along with certain cultivated species into a large
civilized economy, with perpetual change of group and
other adaptation.

But how shall we measure the evolution which proceeds
today, in the so-called "industrial revolution" extending
the humanly controlled economy into mineral nature?
This revolution is occasioned by science, "disinterestedly"
concerned to discover and classify mineral, chemical, and
physical type. Science had its humble beginnings in the
clan rituals, which turned to magic and to liturgical formula
in order to secure the external conditions of group persistence. Astrology gathered a mixture of astronomical and
meteorological fact, with crude hypothesis attempting to
correlate human events with celestial conjunctions. This
early science was utilitarian, but chiefly in the sense that
it looked to nature for moral wisdom, guiding group behavior. It remained associative adaptation. The Greeks
appealed to science for evidence of the existence in man of
a "disinterested" faculty of reason, concerned to know for
the sake of knowledge itself. However, the pragmatist of
today is correct when he insists that knowledge cannot
literally be pursued for its own sake, since whatever is pursued thereby obtains a human value of some sort. The
pragmatic error is to define "utilitarian" too narrowly, and

to see in science only an external adaptation securing survival, overlooking its value as associative adaptation securing group persistence. Science is morally and religiously motivated, and therefore has moral and religious value. This value it is which supports the pursuit of science "for its own sake," even as it supports the pursuit of "art for art's sake."

Prior to modern civilization, science was never consciously pursued for its industrial uses. It was an epochal event, marking the passing of antique civilization and the advent of modern civilization, when the Franciscan scholar, Roger Bacon, in the thirteenth century, taught that science empowers the human body as well as emancipates the human mind. If the domestication of animals and plants inaugurated civilization, what must be the consequence of the domestication of physical nature, advanced by natural science? To what shall lead the cultivation of molecules and atoms, now well begun? What limit shall we set to the power of a group cognizant of the cosmos in its whole extent and in its minutest parts? Shall not man steer the stars in their courses, and that without moving from this earth which is his footstool? Indeed he shall. He shall hold this cosmos in the hollow of his hand. Even now, in ignorance of what he does, he tampers with the levers of cosmic control, and threatens this world with its damnation.

No universal necessity, we have learned, secures the persistence of living matter. There is no universal necessity if there is particular necessity; and science is forever established upon this true dogma which affirms the particular causation of whatever occurs. "Particular causation" means the interaction of individuated things, all different, no two identical. The persistence of group, of type, of form, of structure is particularly determined, as is all extinction of group and type. Yet there is something like necessity—

there is "economic necessity"—which makes the persistence of group and type conditional upon group adaptation. *If* a group or a type is to persist, there must be reciprocal adaptation. However, there is no necessity, cosmic or general or group, absolutely requiring that the group persist. Whether or not the group persists, with persistence or change of type, is the consequence of its individual variants. Yet groups and types have long endured, as determined by their individual constituents. It follows that the individual organism cannot be defined as a unit pursuing its own survival or existence. No living unit secures its indefinite survival; *all that lives is mortal.* What the organism secures, or fails to secure, is progeny, reproduction of type, establishment of group type, persistence of its group. In fact, we must distinguish those individuals which have issue from those which do not. In the former, the factor making for group persistence overweighs the factors making for individual survival. In the latter, it does not. Since life began, there has been provision of individual character securing group persistence. The occurrence of such character has never failed, each yesterday has been redeemed.

Why should we deny, in face of all of the evidence, the continuity of organic evolution with the inorganic evolution of chemical and mineral type? Why do we refuse logic, which tells us that the evidence allows only one inference; namely, that all persistence of type is the index of group persistence, secured by the reciprocal adaptation of variant individuals? We do not have to ascribe "life" to molecules and atoms in order to know that they must be, as actualities, individually variant, and that their individual variation has on occasion established new types. We are prevented from conceiving of the evolution of inorganic type by two antiquated traditions, both of which perpetuate the delusive faith of Greek philosophy in "eternal forms."

One is the atomistic tradition which led to modern chemistry. When geometry was the whole of physics, as it was for the Greeks, it was desirable to find in nature an absolute and indestructible grain, describable in geometric terms. The Greek "atoms" provided this grain; and everything— light, life, perception, even thought—was described as made up of one or another sort of atoms. There are only "atoms and the void," taught Democritus. Modern science appropriated this atomistic conception, but only with all-important reservations. It was seen that the geometry of nature is a *physical* structure which must be empirically discovered. This structure may vary with time and place, i.e. in the particular situation. There is no "geometrical necessity" securing the persistence of atoms. These may disintegrate into radiant energies, and vanish. There is consequently no immutability of atomic type.

However, the geometrical dogma existed in a more potent form, which does not require the eternity of atoms. It is only the geometrical *structure* which persists, taught Plato, everything that individually exists being ephemeral. It was Plato's conception that Roger Bacon recovered and made the basis of modern physics. Bacon saw clearly that geometrical structure is *relational* pattern. Things may come and go; but the interactions of things, determining their appearance or exodus, exhibits always this self-identical relational pattern. However, contemporary science now rejects the dogma requiring fixity of structure. The relational pattern may change in time and vary in space. It is only anachronistic dogma, perpetuated by intellectual inertia, and nothing in contemporary physical theory itself, that prevents us from drawing the implications of the evidence of an evolution of chemical type.

The contemporary physicist, indeed, is the first to assure

us that his theory is statistical in its meaning, and presents in its formulas and constants the mean or average behavior of microscopic populations numbering into the billions of billions. Presumably, these molecules, atoms, electrons, etc., exhibit more or less variety of individual difference. It is necessary, indeed, to take account of different isotypes of the same atomic type, or "element." These microscopic entities, if they vary at all, must vary individually in *all* their properties, reactions, and relationships. They either are not individuated, which is inconceivable, or are individuated through and through. There is really no question that the persistence of physical structure indicates only the uniformity, i.e. persistence of type, of billions of microscopic individuals, all variant and literally identical in no respect. This uniformity is very marked; but it may be either a close uniformity of all of the microscopic particles, or a close uniformity of most of them, with very considerable occasional diversity.

The physicist is prevented from perceiving the implications of his own science by the influence of modern philosophy, which exists for no other reason than to perpetuate the Greek dogma of "eternal structure." This dogma, the philosopher mistakenly thinks, is the sole support of faith in theoretical science itself. Contemporary biology shows us what is true and what false in this belief. The dogma is not needed if the scientist proceeds from his theoretical definition of structure and type to an evolutionary study of the establishment of type; *but it is needed to prevent, belittle, and deprecate that advance* from purely theoretical to evolutionary science. The philosopher is concerned to perpetuate the Cartesian dualism of "matter" and "mind," because this antiquated Cartesian "science" was the basis of all of the later speculation which is his special competence. He cannot admit that the whole of modern philosophy is invalidated by contemporary science and logic. He must live intellectually in the seventeenth century, which defined "matter" as that which is described by eternal geometry, and "mind" as that which eternally knows this geometrically structured "matter." If he should emerge into this twentieth century, to learn that the "persistent problems of philosophy" generated by the "mind-matter dualism" are today removed by science, what will become of his philosophy, what is his professional competence worth? Let scientists know that all contemporary philosophy—all, without exception—is only a befuddled attempt to compel contemporary thought to remain within the limits set by seventeenth century science. This holds even, or especially, of so-called "philosophy of science," as the ridiculous title itself sufficiently indicates. What on earth, in heaven, or in hell might be "philosophy of science"?

There are rare forms, and also abundant forms, of mineral, molecular, and atomic matter. The rarity or abundance of a type indicates the adaptedness of that type to its local habitat. Few molecules can exist in the sun; but a few do, being adapted to that temperature. In the sun there is much atomic disintegration, on earth little. The evolution of physical type at the earth's surface is chiefly that of mineral and organic type. *The evolution of organic type has conditioned that of mineral type,* biology and geology being inseparable. The classification of mineral, molecular, and atomic type in the universe provides data allowing historical retrospect on the evolution of physical type. The atomic "table of elements" shows a periodicity of chemical properties compelling us to arrange atoms in groups, much as living species are arranged in genera. The evolutionary advances from unicellular to multicellular form carried further an earlier evolution which advanced from electrons to atoms, from atoms to molecules, from molecules to crystals and colloids, and from colloids to protoplasm and living organisms.

But is it possible to conceive of atoms or molecules as species, i.e. as groups associated by reciprocal adaptation and evolving through change of adaptive type? It is, if we will clear our minds of the naïvetés of the primitive physics which was Greek atomism. Do we believe that atoms are hard little pellets, indestructible and eternal? Do we believe that the molecules of granite today are the identical molecules which constituted the newly formed granite? Why confuse persistence of type with individual survival? The evidence is that the span of individual existence shortens as we go down the ladder of adaptive type. The evolution of adaptive type has been conditioned by an evolution of development or growth, the more advanced and complex types requiring longer growth. Presumably, there is continuous death and birth of individual molecules and atoms, the "life span" of these being probably a few minutes or seconds. A flame, although it is composed of chemical units incandescent only for a moment, will eat its way through steel. The known properties of physical nature are not the properties of individual things; they indicate the typical and collective reaction of enormous groups of units. Persistence of the group does not indicate the persistence of its individual constituents. How atomic type is reproduced is at present inconceivable; but we are still ignorant of how bacterial type is reproduced, although there is no question of the fact. To the best of our present knowledge, the quantum of the physicist indicates the most elemental, original, and basic type of physical adaptation, that which has been modified in all subsequent readaptation. The quantum is not a thing, but a unit of action or motion or energy, so that it discloses a granular pattern in change itself; but this smallest unit of interaction tells us something of the most minute entities which exist in virtue of such interaction.

The evolution of physical and chemical type has supported the continual increase in quantity of formed matter, and advanced the continuing creation of the cosmos. The mineral, molecular, atomic, electronic, and quantic levels indicate very major readaptations, comparable with that which supported the advance from unicellular to multicellular organisms. The evolution of physical type proceeded more slowly than that of life, the great waves occurring at longer intervals, and the fixation of type being greater and firmer. Just as we may ignore animal evolution in studying human progress, so we may ignore physicochemical evolution in studying organic evolution, or the evolution of subatomic type in studying mineral or geologic evolution. However, we should not forget that human progress is itself an evolution of animal type; organic evolution, one of molecular type (organic molecules are much larger and more complex than those of inorganic matter); and mineral and molecular evolution, one of physicochemical type. *There is, in short, a single evolution, that of adaptive type supporting material increase.*

In our present ignorance of the mechanisms of the reproduction, securing the persistence, of physicochemical type, we can perceive only some of the larger features of its evolution. However, this should not blind us to the significance of the fact that an evolution of material type has occurred. The fact itself informs us that nature in its totality is a moral economy, formed matter of every type persisting only in virtue of reciprocal adaptations of various sorts. All natural science is moral and economic science. The material units of nature, large or minute, are individually better or worse adapted to the conditions of group persistence. Some individuals are more creative, some more destructive, in their consequence. The more destructive ultimately destroy the conditions of persistence for their group and type, so that their type becomes extinct. The chemical atoms and their isotypes indicate well adapted types.

Laboratory analysis has revealed much of the physicochemical structure of matter; and the telescope and spectroscope make possible the chemical analysis of the stars. Chemical analysis is still primarily a dissection of matter into its smaller units; and it challenges and assists, but does not itself undertake, inquiry into how the substances disintegrated in the laboratory were by nature integrated and multiplied. Yet laboratory analysis does give us important clues to the evolution of physicochemical type, especially in its reliance upon heat as the most effective agent of disintegration. Heat breaks down the physical integration which earlier bound gaseous matter into liquid and solid matter. It disintegrates the molecule into its component atoms; it even disintegrates the atom, most evidently in the sun, into subatomic forms of energy. It is impossible not to find in this disintegrative action of heat a clue to the nature of adaptation in physical nature. There, adaptive type is that which serves to prevent the generation of heat, or to make matter tolerant of heat. Physical and chemical type indicate adaptations which keep matter cool.

Why should matter be kept cool? Because "heat" is a sort of movement which, although a degree of such motion is evidently a condition of material activity, quickly becomes destructive. Moreover, there is in matter a universal tendency to generate heat, consequent upon the gravitational attraction which constantly tends to congregate the microscopic units of matter into large masses, when the units exert great pressure upon one another. This pressure induces the rapid vibration which is "heat," measured in temperature; and the vibration can explode the molecule or even the atom. Presumably, gravitation—which may be quite universal, even light gravitating—was an early established adaptation which preserved material units by bringing them together for reciprocal support against disintegrative forces. This adaptation then supported material increase, leading to congestion in the generation of heat-vibration; and there followed the series of chemical and mineral adaptations which prevent units from coming into such close proximity that they exert destructive pressure, generative of heat.

Of these readaptations, the most familiar is circular motion, which appears at all levels. The atom rotates; the moons, planets, and stars rotate. Moons revolve around their planets; planets around their suns; the star revolves in its galaxy; light, in its cosmic circle. The Greeks found in circular motion the elemental motion of nature. We believe circular motion to be compounded of two linear motions. The small and large circular motions of things evidently circumvent gravitational or electrical attraction by means of some second linear motion. For these compounded linear motions we still have no name and know no cause.

A second type of adapation holds atoms apart in the molecule; and another holds apart molecules bound by intermolecular bonds in the lattices of crystals. Crystalline formation is one of three known supermolecular formations. The cooling liquid may crystallize, as heat vibration ceases to mobilize its molecules. It may solidify into an amorphous granular matter which retains many of the properties of liquids. Or it may solidify into a gelatinous colloidal form, in which the molecules are less firmly fixed than in the crystal. Through this colloidal adaptation proceeded the advance to protoplasm and living organisms. All living matter is colloidal, although some viruses pass into and out of a crystalline phase. The crystal form is evidently an adaptation which fixated type, precluding further evolution. Colloids are quasi-solutions, their peculiar properties depending on the remarkable properties of the water molecule, which combines in loose relationship with other compounds to form protoplasm or living matter. The colloidal form is capable of tremendous complication and diverse readaptation. Indeed, the classification of living species is a classification of colloidal types.

The Soviet scientist A. I. Oparin has shown in his study *The Origin of Life* how terrestrial matter may have proceeded through colloidal formations to the origin of living organisms. His intention is to establish the purely mechanistic or chemical character of the evolution. He points out that the peripheral matter of the sun already advances to molecular forms. Such peripheral solar matter, he believes, formed our earth. From his assumptions as to the chemical constitution of this original matter, he proceeds to show how processes would necessarily occur at the surface of the earth leading to the formation of colloids and coacervates, and thence to the enzymes and protoplasm of the primary organisms. Dr. Oparin's reconstruction of this progress is interesting, plausible, and probably close to the truth. However, it should be remembered that he speaks the language of the philosophical materialist. Philosophical materialism is not science, but a form of metaphysics; and metaphysics consistently explains events as due to their own consequences. Thus Dr. Oparin attributes to the solar matter which became the earth all of those properties which are observable in the laboratory today. It is as if a biologist were to "explain" the evolution of living organisms by showing that each adaptive type is a readaptation of its predecessor. This it is; but what we need to know is why one adaptive type persisted, whereas another type became extinct. The chemi-

cal properties which Dr. Oparin attributes to solar molecules are truly adaptive types created later on earth. We
must not telescope later into earlier evolution.

As a matter of fact, it has recently been shown that the
matter of the earth was never part of the sun, the formation
of the sun and the earth having proceeded concurrently.
In other words, the sun is probably no older than the earth.
The matter drawn into the sun was less able to resist
gravitational attraction than that which formed the planets,
so that the superior adaptation of terrestrial matter has
always qualified the earth. It is no accident that the earth
is small and the sun large, and that the planets revolve at
their respective distances from the sun. *Nothing that is
describable is accident; for what is describable has form,
and all form whatsoever is adaptive type of some sort.* Accordingly, to accept as explanatory Dr. Oparin's account
of the origin of life is to preclude, not to provide, the mechanistic explanation of this colloidal evolution. All that has
particularly occurred was predetermined at the beginning
of the world, and long before that; but the fact that all is
particularly determined tells us nothing of the establishment and spread of type. To know why type arises and persists, we must recover the history of reciprocally adapted
groups.

Trained as we are from childhood in philosophical error,
and to the supposition that there has been no evolution of
physical structure, it is difficult to free our minds from
teleological metaphysics. Must we not reconstruct the past
by inference from the present? And does this not require
us to explain the past merely as differently specifying a
form or structure which now observably exists? We must,
and it does. But when the reconstruction is completed, and
we can show that each stage of the evolution of language,
or society, or life, or matter in fact modified a preceding

stage, we must not suppose that we know what *caused* these successive modifications. To know that yesterday was in some respects *like* today is not to know why today is *unlike* yesterday in other respects. All change of type has a general cause, i.e. it is a group change. When we cease to make the existence of type its own explanation, we cease to be philosophers and become scientists; and that is when we begin to ask questions which have empirical answers, more than circumlocutions of the questions. Does light radiate equally in all directions from its source, or does it move only to a material receptor? Is "the conservation of energy" more than insistence upon type and statistical method? What types of matter can exist in interstellar space? Is interstellar space hot or cold, or of no temperature, heat being a condition of formed matter? What is "interstellar space"? Is it chaos? Is the matter of the sun atomic because of its heat, or is the sun hot because of its lack of molecular structure? Shall we attribute to matter that is densely packed, generative of heat, and continually destroyed, the same properties as we attribute to matter at the surface of the earth, which is light, porous, and complexly structured? There are no Bacons, Newtons, and Shakespeares on the sun's surface; yet what we call "life" is an adaptive form, conditioning the persistence and increase of its own type; and living matter is a sort of chemical matter. Can we find evidence that non-living matter is also of such adaptive type as to secure its own persistence and increase? This we can.

Water presents a chemical type of unusual and remarkable properties, all conducive to its own persistence. It is the most powerful of solvents, taking up other chemicals without injury to itself. It is of all things most absorbent of heat, again without injury to itself. It is the great agency of crystallization. Here, as in solution, there is preserved both water and the chemical so combined. Its many remarkable properties make *water the greatest stabilizer of temperature known or conceivable.*

The matter which composes the surface of the earth is unusually light. It holds a high proportion of the lighter metals, contained in light minerals. Lighter atoms exert less gravitational pressure, and generate less heat. These minerals are at the surface because they are lighter, but they are lighter because of their physical and chemical constitution. *The physical properties of matter are conditioned by the chemical constitution of matter.* There are stars of small volume but extremely great mass, composed apparently of atoms which are all heavy nucleus without electrons. The physicist compares them, not very aptly, to collapsed eggshells. These heavy stars will probably generate great heat and explode into diffuse gas. Just as we find organic natural types which were established in every evolutionary period, so, it seems, we shall find in physical nature matter in every stage of evolution. The evolution of matter is still written in the stars. The matter of the earth has presumably, evolved, so to speak, where it now is. *It has always been together.* It has proceeded through successive readaptations, especially at its surface. Here were gathered a group of light elements, in particular hydrogen, oxygen, carbon, and nitrogen, persisting and increasing in virtue of their adaptive properties.

Especially important in geologic history was the action of water, which preserved the earth's surface by keeping it light, porous, and cool. By the film of ocean, with its currents, its cycle of evaporation and rainfall and river, and its effects upon atmosphere, terrestrial water provides a great cooling system, stabilizing temperature. Water worked also in the advances to crystalline and colloidal forms. It next conditioned the spread of colloidal matter, in living organisms, over the dry surface of the earth. Living matter is more than three-parts water; and vegetation is substantially a film of water which shelters the mineral surface of the earth from solar heat. Vegetation converts hard rock into a porous, water-laden soil, regulates the cooling action of evaporation, conditions rainfall, and in every way makes more effective the stabilizing action of water. Except for water and vegetation, the variations of temperature between pole and equator, between summer and winter, between night and day would be much greater than they are. But this geologic evolution, becoming organic evolution, only continues the evolution of physicochemical adaptive type which has conditioned the persistence and increase of formed matter since time began. The earth is better than a fair sample of nature, because it is probably the furthest evolved matter. The evolution of animal and of human type advanced the evolution of physicochemical type. The animals and plants perpetuate a great atmospheric equilibrium, the animals taking oxygen and expelling carbon dioxide, the plants taking this carbon and leaving free oxygen; and their adaptive symbiosis is an important factor in mineral and chemical evolution, resting upon the unusual adaptive properties of the carbon atom. There is continuity between organic and chemical evolution in the large, as well as in the small. The evolution of life is that of the mineral earth. The evolution of the mineral earth is that of life.

What is the place and function of earth in the economy of cosmos? The earth, we are told, is an insignificant speck in the near infinity of space, a peripheral accident, an ephemeral anomaly. This is scientific nonsense, quite unholy wishful thinking on the part of men who guess, yet fear, the terrible and incredible implications of evolutionary science. The earth is not small. *The size of the human organism is just about halfway between the cosmos in its totality, and the smallest effective unit of matter known to exist.* Remembering that the cosmos has been created by its microscopic units, and by no *deus ex machina,* we conclude that the size of a unit is no measure of its creative efficacy, and that man is probably just of a size to give him maximum creative control. To be larger, we know, would embarrass motion, growth, and social progress. We must not confuse the *effective units* of nature, which are submicroscopic electrons, atoms, and molecules and sizable organisms, with the great conglomerations of these units which compose planets and suns. The largest living tree may be the largest unit existing. There has been an evolution of unit-size. We also know that larger units are conditioned in their motions by changes in their parts. The electron conditions atomic motion, the enzyme conditions human development. These small units are to the larger units somewhat as is the human individual to the planet, or even to the galaxy and cosmos.

But, finally, we know that the whole *evolution* of the cosmos, with its galaxies, is the consequence of *single,* individual variations of these small units. From the beginning of measurable time, the whole evolution of matter has been determined by these minute variants. The consequence of an individual is known only in its effects. There was an individual variant which established its living type, to cover the earth with vegetation. *There was an individual variant which stirred in primeval chaos to establish its material type, and to transform chaos, through the eons, into cosmos.*

It is a foolish illusion, every moment discredited, that makes bodily size the measure of a thing's activity and reach. Microscopic causes have cosmic effects. Small are the genes which determine every organic development, and thereby every persistence of group and type. The difference between an earth clothed with life and an earth naked as the moon was once submicroscopic. The destiny of cosmos still lies with its effective units. What is this nature, that man should be mindful of it? This cosmic design is not the work of "cosmic necessity," imposing its form upon the minute ingredients of nature. It is the creation and creature of those ingredients. The cosmos is creature, creators are the minute.

Shall not earth and life and man have a place in this cosmic creation? It is no philosophic fantasy, it is sober scientific hypothesis that sees in earth the governor of this universe, providing by its water and its life that margin which conditions the persistence and increase, forfending the destruction and extinction, of universal matter. Here, on earth, the motions which would generate excessive heat are converted into wind and water current, into living growth, into human industry. Here is what keeps material creation in the black, just out of the red. Here is where congestion due to increase is overcome by rapid and continuous readaptation, securing increase. Man increases life, life makes more effective water, water preserves earth, earth preserves cosmos. Let life cease, and there would begin a decline of universal matter at first imperceptible, but steadily accelerating in its tempo, with catastrophe more frequent, until at last the cosmos would go out in flames. Always, since time began, there has been that *place* where readaptation redeemed cosmos from its own congestion. That place was earth, the redemptive matter is now man. The group which established man was the group which established life; the group which established life was the group which emerged, reproducing an original variant, out of chaos to establish matter. Man is now, because he always was, governor of this world, creator and redeemer of his universe.

Has not the evolution of life always been linear, directed

toward man by the law which makes group adaptation the condition of external adaptability and persistence? Does not the evolution of life extend that same evolution which created all matter? How shall there be two such lines? If man is annihilated, no fixated species will become unfixed, to replace him. If life is annihilated, nowhere else will matter proceed to protoplasm and living type. The fullness of adaptability is only here. The economies of nature and of man are one. The evolution is one. The glory and the terror are one. The creative godhead is one. The inheritance of responsibility and power is linear, father to son. The truth which religious myth saw in a glass darkly, and which idealistic philosophy vaguely lisped, is today by science made clear. Man is the heir of all past time. On his shoulders rests cosmos. In his hands are the controls of creation, now and forever. In his thought, which has no measurable dimension, lies all the destiny there is.

How should it have been otherwise? What else could be conceived? Where should we have sought the Creator? In the heights, in the depths? Or poised between height and depth, there where man stands midway between the cosmos and the quantum, moving the levers of creation. Truly was it said: If you have known the Son of Man, you have known the Father. For other father there is none, nor was there ever. Man, know yourself!

* 8 *

THE KEY TURNED

THE issues which directly divide and threaten mankind are political issues. They are of two sorts, being due either to local national loyalties, or to opposed social ideals. The basic problem is accordingly a moral one. *It is to find that adaptation which will make mankind kin.* Social adaptation is strong enough to support national economies; but it fails to support mankind, by providing the kinship which would bring peoples and national cultures into a civilized society inclusive of all humanity; and the failure exhibits itself especially in a conflict between alternative political programs, objectives, and ideals. It is intellectually agreed that civilization must be built upon a moral foundation, that of universal justice; but communists and individualists differ as to what constitutes justice, and as to how it can be secured. Communists and individualists are equally aware that justice is a relationship between individual and group; but where the communist sees the individual as a member of the group, the individualist sees in the group an outgrowth and support of the individual. This difference of approach results in different programs of government and political economy. However, we must ask whether group adaptation requires uniformity of economic adaptation. Would uniform political economy of itself secure group adaptation, adaptability, and persistence? Perhaps not. But does not *justice* require an equalitarian system of political economy, giving to each individual his equal weight and place? And must there not be one system which best secures this? Is there a value beyond justice? Well, if the quest for justice divides mankind into irreconcilable groups, must not science and moral wisdom look beyond justice, to find what will unify mankind and secure persistence and increase? Can there be justice which is less than mercy, something beyond justice? Can there be justice and mercy without kinship? Is justice, or kinship, our most ultimate necessity?

The quest for justice is as old as civilization. Ancient Egypt, possibly the oldest of the great societies, whose wisdom preserved in the Hebrew Bible came to the modern world, discerned a moral law which generates all lesser good. It was the Greeks who required moral law to be incorporated in civil law, as justice. Their philosophers advanced a theoretical science, ostensibly discovering in nature the eternal structure which in human activity manifests itself in just law. The Greek skeptics, and after them the modern skeptics, rightly objected that theoretical science, descriptive of what eternally is, cannot inform us of what is not but ought to be. Modern thought then advanced to the notion of a *progress* which continually reforms and betters the structure of society; and evolutionary science made this concept of progress universal or cosmic, encouraging inquiry into the progressive creation of natural structure. Not justice, the fixed structure, but group adaptability, securing persistence by means of structural change, must be our goal. Kinship, giving and receiving more than justice, is our need. How far must kinship stretch? How can it be generated?

The religions of the past, and also the science of the past in its initial phase, had insight into the dependence of man upon his natural context. Man must be right with God, or

with nature, they said. But they mistook the character of
this dependence. Human society is not dependent upon
the environment as are natural species. An eminently adaptable group, society carries within itself the power of adaptation to external change. It can only be self-destroyed, by
failure to readapt itself to conditions consequent upon
human activities. Such readaptation is change of group
adaptation, requiring from the individual a larger and
fuller social response to humankind, this being the condition not of individual survival but of group persistence.
But why should the individual prefer the persistence of
the large group to his own survival, to the persistence of his
family and seed, or to that of the local group with which
he is identified?

Civilization has always been a tension between two sets
of forces. One set would carry it onward to larger civilization, and ultimately to a world society embracing mankind; the other would take it back to the clan. Religion
went beyond clan myth in its pursuit of human community,
in its perception that large community is the condition
of human persistence, and in its vague appraisal of the
cosmic significance of human life. Religion taught that the
good life is not "of this world"—meaning this local present
—but is concerned with cosmic destiny; and it strove to
widen social affection to such breadth and intensity as to
make the individual the father and protector of mankind.
Science in its initial advance also had insight into the cosmic
context which gives to the human reason, as ground of human communion, a cosmic function of some sort. But every
antique religion became fixated in orthodoxy under the
pressure of local political and economic adaptation, over-
coming group adaptability; and science too was fixated,
becoming a pursuit of structure and fixed type. With religion and science fixated, modern civilization crystallized

into national groups, which bought social adaptation at some price of social adaptability; and moral inquiry became a game of words and verbal controversy, undirected by scientific and religious insight into the locus of the moral relationship which ties the existence of the individual to the persistence of the group.

What, according to evolutionary science, is good, righteous, moral, just? Ultimately, intrinsically, inalienably good is existence itself. If there be any good whatsoever, existence is a necessary condition of that good. But existence is plural, individuated. Each and every individual existence is therefore a good. The more existences, the better? Even so. *Here is the quantitative criterion* of value, providing a *measure* of value. Secondarily good, supporting intrinsic good and itself derivatively good, is whatever promotes existence. All individual existence is ephemeral, all that *exists* is mortal. Then whatever conditions persistence and increase is derivatively good; and whatever conditions depopulation and annihilation is evil. We know that first adaptation, and finally adaptability, conditions persistence and increase. We have reason to believe that human increase conditions living increase and thereby even cosmic increase. Good, accordingly, is whatever secures human increase and prevents depopulation; and best is the adaptability which conditions readaptation to congestion conditioned by increase. What is this adaptability, required today of man? Is it diversity of genic constitution, or diversity of acquired habit? It is both, because human development, and with it what is acquired during growth, is still genically conditioned. Body and mind are one, not two. The true civilization is a humanity in which there are no political, economic, or cultural barriers to the spread of diverse adaptive type which originates in individual developments, genically and otherwise determined in their individual character and type. Of supreme value in evolutionary science is its advertisement that there is no *general necessity* securing adaptation, persistence, increase; nor is there such necessity compelling depopulation and extinction. Things must be adapted *if* there is to be persistence and increase. Adaptability is a condition of creation; but there need be neither persistence nor creation. This world can be returned to chaos, with the destruction of man, life, and formed matter. *At every moment the decision is made which redeems creation,* and prevents return to chaos; and this decision, today that of man, is made when man finds existence, cosmic and individual, to be good. Not arrogant, and not naïve, was Margaret Fuller when she affirmed her acceptance of the universe. Shallow and boorish was Thomas Carlyle when he laughed: "By gad, she'd better!"

We are not compelled to create. We can destroy. It is our power and privilege to accept or to reject the conditions of individual and cosmic existence. Modern ethics had its first and as yet its only text in the play "Hamlet," which made this question "To be or not to be" its central theme. Hamlet was sick unto death of the evil of this world. Perceptive and good, he knew that the world's disease was his own, the human individual being of cosmic consequence. Some part of this world-sickness was the philosophy which pretended to wisdom, but which only sicklied everything over with its pale mimicry of thought. "To thine own self be true, And it must follow, as the night the day, Thou canst not then be false to any man." What mockery of wisdom, if we are ignorant of what we are, in all our consequence! Was it not dramatic justice that sent Polonius to be skewered behind the arras? "I could be bounded in a nutshell and count myself a king of infinite space, were it not that I have bad dreams," cried Hamlet. And so could we all be, tied to earth but ruling heaven, were it not for our dull dreams. It is our fixation of thought, our verbal pretense of knowledge, our lack of concern, our emptiness of passion that lames us. Not daring to be gods, we become less than healthy beasts. But Hamlet did find truth, in deeds. He cleansed Denmark, paying the price required, embracing the world's evil and going down with it to death. And half a century after Shakespeare came Puritan revolution, cleansing that people of political abomination and establishing the modern commonwealth. For man, to be is to know, to accept, and to enact a destiny individual in its doing but cosmic in its effect. We have no choice but to be god or devil, nor did we ever.

Good is human increase, conditioning every increase; and good is whatever sustains human increase. This provides us with a scientific criterion of value, i.e. a measure of value. There can be no other criterion of value; none has been found, none is conceivable. But the announcement of this quantitative criterion at once arouses objection and even disgust, because it is perceived that sudden increase causes congestion, poverty, and war; and it is not perceived that progress is the readaptation which overcomes or prevents congestion, allowing increase. This earth can even now support a larger human population than it bears. The congestion and poverty of today are not due to lack of external adaptation and material resources. They are due to lack of social adaptability, adjusting group adaptation under change of conditions induced by man himself. Adaptability is a *present* condition, although its fruits are future. But when we approach the question of social adaptability, the sufficiency of which is peace and industry and increase, we are met by all those orthodoxies of habit and belief which fixate group adaptation and cultural type. These cultural fixations resemble the genically determined fixations of plant and animal species, in that they condition temporary persistence with loss of adaptability, securing the near at the cost of the further future.

Yet these diverse cultures, with what is relatively fixated in them and what is adaptable in them, must be woven into the great society of the future. The evolutionary science directing this creative work will not discount the associative adaptations which have brought the peoples of earth as far as they have come. There is no formula defining the adaptable group in its eternal political-economic and other structure. The adaptable population is structurally plastic, by definition. The adaptable society is one that *readapts* its type to changing human conditions. The progress to full civilization must be a continual readaptation of group habits, i.e. cultures and economies which at any and every time exist. These local patterns are the material which must be woven into the society of mankind. The science of man is both theoretical and historical. It first discovers structure; but, behind each diverse local structure and type, it discovers the history which made it what it is. Its aim is to learn progressively, with perpetual readaptation of itself, what will *contain* these cultural diversities without harm to the populations they support, and with benefit to all. Knowing the past evolution of cultures, it will learn how each society may come within the civilized community of mankind.

This appeal to cultural evolution must not become an appeal to history as such, with substitution of "historical interpretation" for causal analysis. The fact that all natural history is the work of individual variants, able to establish cultural types, does not alter the fact that what can be established is always *adaptive type* securing group persistence. Just as surely as the *genic* combination of reproductive with highly specialized external adaptation conditions the fixation and extinction of animal and plant species, "external selection" canceling "internal selection" and destroying adaptability, so there is combination and fixation of *acquired habits* in the human group, which thereby secures persistence and increase at the cost of adaptability. Indeed, we need history chiefly to detect, and to avoid, the combinations of internal and external adaptation which prevent civilized progress. *Progress is perpetual war with dogma, l'idée fixe.*

The *internal* adaptation of the human group has been that which extended domestic habit in group kinship to clan, tribe, nation, empire, and large religious confession. *External* adaptation has been that of the group to other human groups and to the nonhuman environment. Our terminology is inadequate to keep these three sorts of adaptation distinct. The term "political" covers both the first and the second adaptation, because the individual's reactions to other groups are implemented by government, which also effects his intragroup response. The term "economic" covers both the first and the third sort of adaptation, because the use of material resources is regulated by law, which again implements intragroup habit. Thus all current terminology conspires to confuse the three sorts of adaptation, as if there were but one, that which is implemented by government; and kinship is confused with every sort of good and bad adaptation to other groups, and even with our individual adaptation to material things. So there arises a new myth, characteristic of our time, identifying human character and all type with political economic structure. From this modern myth springs a pseudoscientific or philosophical controversy, debating whether economic history is politically determined, or political history is economically determined. In fact, the determinants of human history have been and will continue to be individual genic inheritance, domestic upbringing, social or cultural education, and the relations among groups—all these factors occurring individually and typically. But group adaptation also generated religion, art and science, which looked beyond the state; and, on the other hand, there persisted within every political association minority groups, and there also were generated newly fixated classes and professions.

Before Karl Marx, the modern world identified human history with political history. The historian accepted the Greek metaphysics which defined man as the *political animal*, the species which lives under government. The Greek tradition made for hyperdevelopment of certain external adaptations to other groups, in nationalism; and it also led to the present ideal of world government as the needed alternative to nationalism. It threw us into this political age, which defines society solely in terms of its political institutions. Marx attempted to correct the error, by placing emphasis upon economic institutions. He pointed out that the primary business of government is the regulation of group economy, either in order to fixate economic habit, or, on occasion, to effect its readaptation and reform. Marx perceived that the evolution of economic adaptation (which is to things) proceeds in some independence of other evolution of type, yet conditions all other progress. He distinguished three successive stages of economic evolution: agricultural, commercial, and industrial. He explained human history wholly as the consequence of economic evolution, which has its epochal effects upon political, social, and other adaptive type. In short, he saw in civilized progress an evolution primarily of the external adaptation of the individual to his *nonhuman* environment.

The Marxist doctrine was a needed corrective of the earlier political interpretation, which made civilized progress an evolution of external adaptation to other human groups. However, neither interpretation of history paid much attention to the evolution of internal adaptation and social adaptability, which is the controlling factor in all human progress, primitive or civilized. The Marxist interpretation, in recognizing economic adaptation, conceived this economic relationship to be virtually independent of other adaptive evolution. Although Marx was pre-Darwinian, he seems to have thought of economic evolution as the result of an external selection exerted upon man by the physical environment, which brought about political and cultural readaptations internal to society. This doctrine mistakes the true direction of economic evolution, which proceeds from the group outward, first in the domestication of animals and plants extending *group* adaptation to other living species, and today in the science and industrial progress which extends the same adaptation to mineral nature. The Marxist philosophy is materialist in name rather than in insight. In fact, it makes the outgoing attention of man to animals, plants, and material nature the dynamo of social evolution. But it does thereby discount the evolution of social and interhuman adaptation.

However we define the terms "political" and "economic," the persistence, progress, and increase of every human group are at once politically and economically conditioned. Man had no sooner moved to cultivation than he found his agricultural economy in need of external defense and internal regulation; and the progress to artisanship and commercial economy required and received continual legal and political support. True in Marx was his perception that this economic progress, securing increase, led to and was conditioned by other political and social readaptation, society being chronically divided between those who favored such readaptation and those who resisted it. The destiny of society was largely determined by the changing fortunes of this conflict.

But what decides the issue of the conflict? Why have some societies remained agricultural, others remained agricultural-commercial? Why did Chinese commerce thrive only to decline and lapse again? Why did the Mediterranean economy commercialize first Europe and then other continents? Why did science thrive only in the West, and precipitate industrial revolution only in the far West? *Because the controlling progress,* in civilized as in primitive man, and in human as in animal evolution, *is that of adaptation internal to the group.* Some societies have been or become more *kin,* more socialized and domesticated, than others. Some societies have become less, and other societies have become more, crystallized and fixated in the reciprocal adaptations of their members. Group habit was hardened into tong, caste, feudal rank, upper and middle and lower class, etc. The commercial progress of the Orient was paralyzed by an emphasis upon blood kinship which refused to extend domestic fraternity beyond the large consanguineous group. The caste system fixated economy by its identification of vocational groups with endogamous groups. China and India present two ways in which the socialization of the large population was allowed to proceed only to a certain point, there to remain fixed. Feudalism similarly attempted to hold up the socializing process, by stratifying society within endogamous functional classes, each with its special social responsibility.

This *combination* of external adaptation, economic and vocational, with domestic adaptation is not without disastrous consequence. It means that any major economic change endangers the domestic unit, which is still and always the prime condition of reproduction and group persistence. Fixated societies are reminiscent of insect colonies in their close reliance upon blood kinship for group persistence. *They cease, indeed, to be societies.* They become a plurality of families or kin groups, each group a large family or endogamous clan, adapted to other groups only externally as are animal and plant species, group adaptation being replaced by economic adaptation. They are dependent upon the national economy for their economic adaptation and persistence, yet they contribute nothing to it in the way of association. They take the large national economy to be a state of nature, and bemoan its decline and collapse, ignorant of their part in its ruin.

The true society, on the other hand, is still a mating group or breeding population, bound by the association which conditions gene exchange. The human group is not dependent for its adaptability upon variety of genic type as is the animal group; yet it has and needs this genic variety, which continues to condition and to diversify all individual development. But the human group is completely dependent for its adaptability upon the variety of acquired habit developed in the home; and the feudal or other custom which makes of a people a plurality of endogamous groups contained within a single national economy destroys social adaptability, and necessarily fixates economic and political pattern. The society is adaptable, and consequently readapted, only within the limits of this economic system. Only a revolution which breaks up such a combination of domestic with economic adaptation can restore to a people its life and adaptability. The true society is one in which the acquired characters developed in its families are pooled, to become a reservoir of diverse type which supports readaptation of every sort, both internal and external, both political (to other groups) and economic (to nonhuman things).

History presents every sort of social combination and fixation. Among the peoples which entered into and contributed to western civilization were the Jews. Remarkable is the history of this social group, which persisted through all the great civilizations that have been. What was its strength? Was it monotheistic religion? It is true that the Jews took and preserved much that was good in the religions of the great civilizations through which they passed; yet Judaism, in itself, is awe-inspiring not so much for those borrowed theologies as for its intense and living *group-memory*. To this day at their Passover the Jews come shuddering out of Egypt, to this day they weep by the waters of Babylon! Nowhere else do we find comparable group-longevity. Yet Judaism, although not the damnation, is the veritable purgatory of the Jews, at once their curse and their blessing, their weakness and their strength. Its strength is its insight into the nature of the group with its conditions of persistence. The Jews were and are a mating group, allowing no economic, political, or cultural difference to affect the biological association securing group adaptability. Adaptable they have been, accommodating themelves to every empire that has arisen to fall again. *Their religion is strong because it keeps them kin.* As "seed of Abraham" are they kin, whether in historical fact their ancestors were Hebrews, Syrians, Goths, Armenians, or Copts. A race they are not. This strength is also their weakness and their curse, because it forbids them to lose themselves collectively or individually in any society not their own. They are, yet are not, of civilization and mankind. They are something apart, a clan among nations, a tribe among peoples, elected to bear witness to the truth that every empire must fall, every nation destroy itself, and every people pass away, that trades kinship for lesser goods. To-day, there are Jews who would nationalize Jewry in Zion.

Is this the end of the long wandering in the wilderness? But Judah is not and cannot be a nation. Judah is a tribe elected to bear witness to a *universal* truth. It is a truth to be compounded into that science which must support the civilization of mankind. Only when humanity is come home can the Jews be at home. Until then they must be alien still, looking to the promised land, entering not yet.

That kinship cannot be nationalized, that nations cannot forcibly be made kin, Germany has shown. There was a people that made pretense of blood kinship, to bolster up, under hard external pressure, a lack of group adaptation and true kinship. Denial of civilization was the Germans' atavistic idolatry of blood and race! Civilization is what requires each solitary individual, arriving at adolescence, to take his place in the great society of the culturally kin, being about his Father's business of creation, putting aside the ties of blood and race. Let those who have reached nationhood, which at least acknowledges a kinship wider than known consanguinity, not return to race and blood! Society is born of blood and genes in the home, it is true; but its vital movement is outward, toward all men, bringing families and peoples into larger group association. Civilization must recover the kinship of that association which originally established man on earth, and which was then temporarily dispersed into clan and tribe and race. Civilization gathers up and restores the mutilated god, torn and scattered into a thousand races. Civilization is mankind made kin again, and kind.

Nation and empire did much to advance human progress. Political loyalty was and is real virtue, supporting political economies of increasing size, complexity, and endurance. Ancient Rome was not without religion; but in its maintenance of empire it showed the capacity of purely political power. However, it is not accident that secular

Rome—for its later myths were but afterthoughts—gave place to a "Holy Roman Empire," lieutenant to a "universal" church. Political power has seldom long persisted without help from religious devotion, which ties the individual to something more than his political group.

What says an evolutionary science of religion today? The evolutionary scientist must acknowledge the part which religion has played in past progress, where it induced advance from the small primitive community to the large civilized society. It must acknowledge the insight of religion into the bond between the individual and the group, into the cosmic significance of human destiny, and into the temporal creation of the world. It was Judaic and Christian creationism that carried the theoretical philosophy derived from Greece to the empirical method and evolutionary orientation of contemporary science; and it was the Christian acknowledgment of the power and sanctity of the individual that propelled the modern movement of political revolution and social progress. Religion and rationalistic philosophy came together, to lead the individual to his assumption of universal responsibility; and no science which is less than religious in its devotion, courage, and cosmic insight and commitment can be either true or efficacious. Science must be all that religion was; but it must be more. No existing religion will support the advance now required of us, if we are to persist.

Evolutionary science must distinguish the founders of religion from the dogmatic creeds and ecclesiastical institutions which were established to spread and implement the living truth, but which have remained to obscure, fixate, and pervert it. The founders of the great religions— Confucius, Gautama, Moses, Socrates, Jesus, Mohammed, Francis of Assisi—were individual variants whose direct impact upon their fellows was so powerful, and of such sort, as to establish new types of human response, supporting new and larger societies. They, above all, have been the creators of the world and the spearhead of evolutionary progress. But their individual identity must not be confused with that of the type which they severally established in the societies which they came to redeem. This is to mistake effect for cause. The creeds and priesthoods which took their name and authority from these creative individuals were less shaped by them than by current adaptive habit. Gautama was not Buddha while he lived. Gautama was atheist and nihilist, living denial of all orthodoxy. Socrates was not post-Socratic philosophy, which claimed to *possess* the truth Socrates could only and always *pursue.* Jesus was not Christ while he lived. What Jesus taught was quickly paganized into Greek philosophy, pre-Christian cult, and Roman ecclesiasticism. *Of necessity, orthodoxy and ecclesiasticism destroy the living truth and usurp the living power,* fixating what makes adaptable into what is adapted. Let us no longer confuse religious truth with its perversions; for religious truth and science are one and the same. "You believe in God? Then believe also in me, for the Father and I are one. If you have seen me you have seen the Father. Now be as I am, son of man, God and very God. For God is every man that will be about his Father's business, and take up the work of creation." Could it be said plainer? Nineteen centuries of Christian orthodoxy refused to hear, putting the idol Christ into the place of Jesus of Nazareth, crucifying that living truth in their hearts, crying Lord! Lord! even while they denied God where he is, and where Jesus pointed to him, in every son of man that finds creation good and carries on its work. But let us now be taught by science to bring understanding, more than lip service, to those who gave us life, and mind, and religious and scientific truth!

The great orthodoxies have become impediments to progress and human brotherhood. They set Hindu against Mohammedan, Christian against Jew, Catholic against Communist, Protestant against Catholic. They are divisive, not cooperative. They dismember man and cosmos, they tear apart the living god.

True religion is not and cannot be established religion. That is a contradiction in terms. True religion is the living truth which falsifies every creed, even in acknowledging its partial truth and error. The bible of religious truth is written in every language, it speaks in every tongue. True religion knows no pride of race, class, nation, culture, family, profession, confession. It is scornful of pride, especially of that last vanity, shield of ignorance and fear, which is orthodoxy. Blasphemous and protestant the truth must always be. But it is no more humble than it is proud, knowing itself and none other to be Lord of Lords and King of Kings, even that verity which is God, Creator of all that is. Perpetual must be our conflict with those who fixate the living truth into dead superstition, the better to enslave men and give to time its stop.

There are, in every land, many who bear witness to this truth in their *pursuit* of it; for in a world busy with creation knowledge can be only pursuit, not possession. These are the true followers of reason, who find brother and sister in every man and woman, and who are father and mother to all the children born and to be born. Religion is this pursuit of mundane truth, it is no theological sublimation. Rational is the science which convicts theology and philosophy of error in the confusion of kinship with identity of type. *Kinship is what associates difference,* not what associates likeness. What associates like only with like is pride, vanity, self-adoration in a mirror. The group which knows glory and power and government forever is kin to all, it casts

out none, not even one. True science does not confuse type
and structure with the real and living. It knows that structure is retrospect, not prospect, achievement, not goal.
True science knows that nature persists only with change
of structure, preserving the association which make man
and nature kin.

Why should one wish to be kin, and love one's brothers?
Why, it might be asked, does one love one's children? Because this is natural, the desire to persist in one's seed and
type being instinctive and constitutive. Then we should
desire indefinite persistence, in children's children's children who are finally no more our bodily descendants than
everyone's. But indeed we love our children for the joy that
was their creation, before and after birth, in conception and
nurture. In love alone is *joy,* of which pleasure and happi-
ness are but faint and comfortable echo. However, there
are dimensions of passion, intensities of joy, a whole gamut
of being. Our reach lengthens, until it is concern with
cosmic creation in all the future. Concerned with Cosmos
we always were in some degree; but now, through science,
we take deliberate hold of the levers of creation, knowing
our handiwork. Shall we still know joy, larger and more
intense? Shall we now, seeing what the god in us has done,
shrink back in fear, recant from creative joy? Or shall we
find our creation good, even as on that first day, and take
delight in it? Let there again be light, life, joy, man and
nature's increase! Let creation work!

✳ 9 ✳

THE DOOR IS OPEN!

(*Russia and the United States*)

WHAT must we do to be saved? Today this ancient question has a scientific answer. We must establish the association of kinship binding all societies into mankind. This may seem impossible, in a world torn by religious, political, and class division. But the question is not an academic one. The association is that which must be established *now*, at this moment. Tomorrow may be too late. It must seize upon and readapt what now, at this moment, exists. But that is a medley of religions, a chaos of conflicting ideologies. No, it is not. Man has come a long way, by means of his mixture of religious myth, philosophical myth, and natural science toward an establishment of world civilization upon a truth which is at once religious, philosophical, and scientific. Indeed, he has reached the goal appropriate to this time, or he would have reached it if he were aware of where he stands. The United States and Soviet Russia can establish the association which will now, at this moment, secure peace, persistence, progress, indefinite increase. *Sufficient to the day is the good thereof.* The association which can be now established will not remain unchanged in all the future. It will be continuously readapted and bettered; but it can be established, for the first time in the history of man and creation, *now*.

It is established with the advance of the United States and Soviet Russia to mutual respect. This is its sole condition. We have learned that destiny lies wholly in human hands. Only man can provide or withhold the mechanisms effecting progress or destruction. We know that there can be no standing still, that what is not increased is necessarily destroyed. We see that the progress to world civilization is required of us as the consequence of external readaptation in economic industrial revolution, which makes peace the condition of persistence. We see that this economic readaptation makes immediately disastrous the further dependence upon national group-adaptation, with its shortened loyalties and its infection of fear. We see that human progress has already led to larger loyalty in social and political ideals, advancing types of political economy which cross all national lines. Finally we see that this progress leaves us today with individualist and communist democracy, the two faiths of which the United States and Soviet Russia are the protagonists. It does not need to be argued that, if the two faiths proceed to conflict, there will be collapse of civilization, and possibly general destruction; nor that the two peoples, if they will live in peace with one another, can and must bring humanity into peaceful and progressive economy. The work is already done, unless it is all undone by the reciprocal destruction of these two types of political economy. The work is done if we have the scientific insight to see that *association,* or group-adaptation, *is not itself a type of political economy,* although it is conditioned by and again conditions all political economy. Indeed, we must see that the association which binds mankind must generate new types of political-economic adaptation, i.e. political economy, so that it cannot be itself, nor require, a single type of political economy. *Communist and individualist economies must always coexist, side by side.* This duality of political economy was and is contained within the very bowels of nature, which persists only in *groups* of *individuals,* in plurality of every sort.

We are all aware that the economic readaptations of the last century, those of the industrial revolution, have shaken and destroyed all earlier political adaptation, requiring *major social* readaptation. Our error is to believe that some economic adaptation itself can provide the social readaptation which is now required. The fact that the economic adaptation can persist only if the needed social (group) adaptation is forthcoming does not mean that economic will of itself generate social readaptation. *It will not.* The industrial revolution is an effect of natural science, and is not merely economic adaptation. It is an extension to nature of the interest and concern which was and is association or group adaptation; and *the same science which produced the industrial revolution must now recondition group adaptation,* to allow it to support an economic readaptation to external nature. This science instructs us that a single, fixed pattern of political economy must leave man unadaptable, and doomed to extinction. It removes the dreadful error that would condemn mankind to continual warfare.

There are three distinct sorts of adaptation, always and everywhere. In man, they appear in group adaptation, internal to the group; in external or intergroup adaptation, between or among human groups; and in economic adaptation to external nonhuman nature. All human history is interplay among the three distinct adaptations of individuals to their groups, to other groups, and to external nature. Just to distinguish these diverse adaptations, as they work in any society, is to understand the history of that society. For example, recent European history centers in

Germany, which attempted to advance to major economic readaptation in scientific industry without internal readaptation of its own political and social habit, which it kept feudal. The result was that Germany in its rapid increase exerted intense pressures upon neighboring societies, which inevitably reacted with equal and opposite pressures. The progress could have been peaceful if Germany had been readaptable in its relations with other peoples; but a feudal fixation, an internal adaptation which kept it militarily disciplined at home and aggressive abroad, prevented this. Germany became a barracks, subject to profound demoralization in its vital domestic sources. The young rebelled against their *Feldwebel* fathers, joining patricidal and homosexual societies. It was a demoralized people that proceeded twice to suicidal war, dragging all of Europe with them to poverty and destruction. The fathers had eaten sour grapes, and the children's teeth were set on edge.

But Germany is only a terrible and tragically extreme illustration of the process now demoralizing the world, which fails to keep pace with external economic readaptation in its internal social readaptation. *Required is the readaptation which will make the United States and Soviet Russia an associated group.* How much or how little change does this require? Does it require their political economic uniformity, one of the two systems destroying the other? Or does it require their political economic duality? It requires the latter, each people not only tolerating but willingly supporting the other.

Human progress has been the advance to larger society through clan, tribe, nation, empire, religious confession. The central progress has been that of group adaptation, keeping the group adaptable politically and economically. All history shows either this progress, or its failure resulting in decline. For example, the history of the European nations, and of their settlements on other continents, was determined wholly by the internal group habits of these peoples, as they were established at the collapse of medieval society. The Protestant peoples invariably progressed, with political and economic readaptation. The Catholic or Orthodox peoples, dominated by priesthoods, invariably declined, their ecclesiastical pattern requiring feudal polity, and this a backward agricultural economy. The *degree* of ecclesiastical fixation determined the *degree* of backwardness, Spain being more backward than France. *The people is essentially its group adaptation,* which conditions its other adaptation, political and economic. The individuals of progressive and backward groups are of different type with respect to their responses within the group. (This does not exclude the possibility of progressive minorities in backward societies, nor of backward minorities in progressive societies.)

This means that progress is secondarily, not primarily, that of political economy. *Primary is group adaptation.* And this means that *there can be association among political economies of different type.* The association creates group type, not vice versa. The United States and Soviet Russia can be associated. They are associated the moment each society respects the other, acknowledging it as the vehicle of political-economic progress.

It is intellectual folly, bequeathed by the rationalistic eighteenth century, to believe that all humans are necessarily or properly of one type. True reason is the adaptability which transcends old and creates new type. *Association bridges diversity of type.* This explains the coexistence of male and female, positive and negative charge, nucleus and cytoplasm, proton and electron, group and individual. And this explains why, so long as there is type and political economy, there must be diversity of type and political

economy. The conflict between the United States and
Soviet Russia stalemates progress and ensures destruction
because the association of the two peoples, with their
diverse economies, is the condition of persistence without
fixation and ultimate extinction. A society which was
permanently defined and confined within a type of political economy, i.e. a type of external adaptation, could not
endure. The society which can endure will present
diversity of *all* type. It is modern philosophy, perpetuating
medieval theology, that prevents scientific insight into this
needed diversity of type. The advance from philosophy to
science is the advance to peace and civilization.

It is not an accident, of course, that the advance to
civilization should have taken divergent courses to diverse
types of political economy, respectively individualist and
communist. It is not accident that makes the United States
and Russia, after the convulsions of a bankrupt nationalism
destroyed by its self-generated congestions, the protagonists
of progress, committed to the establishment of the world
peace that will allow economic progress. Hegel was not altogether without evidence when he concluded that human
progress, in moving along the dimension of time, had also
moved in space. The civilizations of the Orient and the
Occident may not differ in age; but the progress of civilization, which is continual flight from fixation, most evidently
proceeds from the Mediterranean civilization of antiquity
to its consequence in the modern civilization of today. However, the belief in a single, necessary human type, the
rational man, derives especially from the Greeks; and with it
goes the assumption that the rational man necessarily inhabits a society of one type, the rational habit of the individual reappearing in the structure of the society founded
on reason.

It cannot be denied that uniformity has been a governing modern ideal, impelling modern progress. Yet it should be noted that the Greeks, who gave us this bias, did not themselves follow it. Rather than sink their civic independence and merge their civic differences in national uniformity, they went to ground. Further, the movement to modern civilization, although heavily fraught with Greek philosophy, was not just that movement of itself: it combined faith with reason, putting faith first. Out of this complex of *faith with reason* came the modern mind with its modern science and modern government. Pure reason must bow to particular observation and hypothesis, said the modern thinker. The structures of thought and of society are in continual change. However, let us now observe that the movement from Greek antiquity to the modern world took two routes. One was by way of Rome to western Europe and America. The other was by way of Byzantium and northern Europe to the Russia of today.

What we describe in any evolutionary description is some progress of adaptive type. Antecedent to all adaptive progress, we found, is progress in group adaptation. Human progress is a progress of human association, conditioning further external adaptation. The progress from antique to modern civilization was by way of Christendom, the civilization which followed the collapse of the Mediterranean society politically unified by imperial Rome. But Christendom became two societies, it did not remain one. In the fourth century the emperor Constantine moved his capital from Rome to Byzantium, now Constantinople; and there began the train of events leading to the present schism between communism and individualism. Rome remained the ecclesiastical capital of the Empire, its bishop being pope; but the western half of the Empire rapidly disintegrated while the eastern half stood firm; and the eastern churches later seceded from Rome to form the

Greek Orthodox Church centered at Constantinople. Their secession was theoretically based upon a difference of views concerning the relationship of church and state. The Roman Church maintained the supremacy of the church over the state, seeing in the imperial power a delegated authority subject to itself; and on this basis it justified its assumption of secular powers let fall by the Empire. But the Greek Church held the ecclesiastical and imperial powers to be coordinate, church and state being equally the vehicles of divine authority.

Western Europe was Christianized by the Roman Church, which remained its educator and guardian for ten medieval centuries. Then came conflict between emperor and pope, raising the question of the division of power, and bringing medieval society to collapse. There followed the Protestant Reformation, which disestablished the Roman Church in most of northern Europe. The question of the redisposition of the power earlier exercised by Rome kept Europe in chaos for two centuries; and the power of the church was variously redisposed, usually being usurped by local princes. However, the Protestant reformers had not intended to transfer religious authority to secular rulers. They still held the secular state to be subordinate to a higher moral authority; and they came to locate that authority in the reformed congregation, or even in the religious individual. In more than one instance, this transfer of authority was actually effected, by means of political revolution disestablishing feudal tyrannies and securing sovereign power to the people.

In Britain, a Puritan revolution defeated the monarchy which had usurped religious authority, and put a republican government in its place. This first modern commonwealth failed; and a second revolution demanded only a limitation of monarchical power. But a third revolution was fought by American colonists, descendants of refugees who had fled Europe to escape from feudal and ecclesiastical tyrannies. These colonists had waited only until they were sufficiently strong to secede from Britain, in order to re-establish a republican commonwealth, that which became the United States of America. *To understand the character and history of the United States, one must remember that this society is the issue of the Protestant Reformation,* which religiously required the limited and derivative status of secular power, holding this to be delegated to government by the religious and moral individual. The medieval principle which located supreme authority in the church was perpetuated, in modified form, in the modern principle which locates this authority, carrying with it political sovereignty, in the individual, all corporate and collective power thereby becoming delegated, revocable, and limited. Some two millennia of religious and cultural history therefore commit the people of the United States to the principle of individual authority and sovereignty; and upon this principle is firmly established their whole political economy and culture.

Another history, no less Christian but very different, issues in the Soviet Russia of today. A thousand years ago the leaders of Russia, then a small state, led their people into the Greek Church. A millennium of Christian education followed, during which Russia expanded into the geographically enormous state it is today. Long education in the Byzantine tradition firmly established the tenet that church and state are coordinate powers, equally implementing the absolute authority of God. These medieval centuries transformed the peoples of the barbaric north into Holy Russia, an intensely religious society bound into effective community by church and state at once.

Russian medievalism began, and ended, four centuries

later than that of western Europe. It endured until 1917, when a revolution wiped out both the czarist feudalism and a degenerate ecclesiastical system. However, the revolution could not transfer ecclesiastical power directly to the individual, as the Reformation had done in western Europe. The Greek Church had been too closely identified with the czarist state to allow of that; and with its disestablishment its moral authority inevitably devolved upon the new state, established by the revolution. Russia had always been Holy Russia, sanctified for a thousand years as the true manifest of divine and omnipotent power, and by this faith led to enormous growth. The revolution did not erase veneration for the state, so deeply incorporated in social habit. But Holy Russia became Soviet Russia. The present is still the past, refashioned. It is not entirely new.

Modern societies, emerging from medieval society, did so in virtue of, and as directed by, the type of group or social adaptation they had acquired during the medieval centuries. In western Europe, the supremacy of the church had prevented the advance of imperial power, and held Europe ecclesiastically unified but politically inchoate, the power of the pope being dependent upon an unstable balance of secular powers delegated to kings and princes. The papacy, however, went down with the Empire, leaving Europe to become a plurality of sovereign peoples, each proceeding along its own evolutionary route as determined by its "national culture," i.e. its associative or group adaptation. The destinies of the nations were severally determined by their respective disposition of religious authority and secular power. Where a people remained priest-ridden, it went into steady political and economic decline, its fixity of social adaptation fixating all other adaptation. In the degree that peoples protestantly assumed religious and moral responsibility, they proceeded to political reform and economic progress.

Very different was the Russian reformation. The coordination of ecclesiastical and imperial power had raised no religious issue and generated no conflict. Group adaptation had steadily strengthened and widened; but this progress appeared in the steady expansion of the society, which grew to continental size, supported by a minimum of political and economic readaptation, but by a maximum of group loyalty. So came into being Russia, which in the twentieth century proceeded at once to political reform and to religious reformation. Its religious communism is not a theory, Marxist or other. Its communism is its group adaptation, the devotion and loyalty of the individual to society, and the determination to make group loyalty the source of, giving impetus and direction to, all external adaptation. Political economy must be what is required by, and what supports and further strengthens, group adaptation. The unity of the primitive commune, it is insisted, must be retained within civilization, however large, by means of ever stronger association.

It is exactly in their difference that we discover the deepest bond between Soviet Russia and the United States. The two peoples occupy leading positions for the same reason. Each carries farthest, but in a different direction, the moral progress, that of group adaptation, which was inculcated by a thousand years of medieval religion. They are also alike today in their "irreligious" or Protestant determination to make the moral adaptation inculcated by their earlier religious training the rule of life and the foundation of society, controlling political economy. These two societies, it is not too much to say, are genuinely and preeminently Christian, not in word but in deed. It is in their practice that the character of the individual variant which was Jesus of Nazareth has most widely and surely established its type, the one society finding the actuality of God in the individual, the other finding it in the community; and *each is right, if both are taken.*

This protestant community associating the peoples of Russia and the United States should not be overlooked. Has the United States forgotten its own protestant origins in that struggle which established political liberty as the condition of moral liberty, the political sovereignty of the individual being required to implement the religious responsibility of the individual? The tolerance which this people brings to all religious confessions, the respect which it accords to each and every religious conviction should not be mistaken for moral and religious indifference. The institution of private property is not prized for its own sake, its abuses and its dangers do not go unmarked. It is valued for its needed implementation of individual political sovereignty, which in its turn implements the moral and religious responsibility of the individual. Neither people should underestimate the continuing power of the protestant faith which directed this evolution of individualist political economy. As the people of the United States proceeded to civil war, forbidding the peaceful secession of those who would reestablish feudal economy within its borders, so we may be sure that it will confirm in all of the future, with proper resolution, the protestant liberty of thought and religion which is the ground and reason of its political and economic individualism.

Lacking the evolutionary science which distinguishes true religion from its betrayal, which provides ethical truth, and which shows history to be the moral progress or the immoral retreat which it always is, modern society has confused itself with false doctrine, metaphysical and skeptical. This doctrinaire intellectualism, covering ignorance of social actualities, more than anything else makes communism and individualism seem so flatly incompatible. Individualist democracy, neglectful of its Protestant origin, never did find a theoretical basis for its political faith. Turning from its earlier religious vocabulary, it used the language of philosophy to argue the existence of inalienable rights invested in the individual "by the law of nature and of nature's God." Just what were or are these "natural rights," in the plural? *There is but one natural right, source of all derivative rights.* All rights are powers; and the sole rightful power is the power of the individual to exercise moral responsibility for all men, and therewith for all that exists. This was and is a religious power, whatever we please to call it. Is it not man's responsibility for creation? The right is invested in the individual; it is thereby invested in the community of individuals. But the theorist, seeking a secular vocabulary, conceived the rights to be just political powers, and thereby came into a dilemma; for it is evident that political power in this day and age is that which comes to the individual through his citizenship in some state, the government of which may implement his will at home and exercise it in dealings with other peoples. Thus, the concept of an absolute inalienable *political* right carried implications which seemed to require the fixity, sovereignty, and absolute power of the state.

To avoid such implications, the liberal theorist placed special emphasis upon property rights, which he deemed to be prior to and independent of all other rights. The reason for the sanctification of private property was the hard experience that a government is subject to popular control only if, and exactly so far as, government is dependent upon public appropriations, made to it for specific purposes. It was only by their control of the national exchequer that the British people brought their monarchs under popular control; and it was on the ground that their lack of representation allowed them no political powers that the American colonies justified their secession from Britain, this being reason enough. It is undeniable that the exercise of individual political power is dependent upon the possession of individual economic power, secured by the institution of private property. A government which owns property, or which has such administrative control over economic powers as virtually to possess property, is exactly in that degree beyond any human control whatsoever; and the true constitution of a people, which is only too often far from its written constitution, may be learned at a glance by observing how its government obtains its moneys. But this economic individualism, or institution of private property, is properly prized as a condition of political individualism, the equal distribution of political power; and political individualism is properly retained as a condition of moral or social individualism, which is the right and duty of the individual to participate in the direction and progress of all society. To prize the institution of private property as a condition of the individual assumption of moral responsibility is not to sanctify private property, nor to place corporate property out of public control. On the contrary, it is to require the prevention of unequal distribution of property and economic power, in order to secure the equal distribution of political power. The people of the United States cannot nationalize or communize property, because this would deprive the individual of political power implementing his moral responsibility; but there is no limit to its regulation of economy in the communal interest. There is nothing to prevent the people of the United States and Soviet Russia from the pursuit of identical objectives, to be reached by different political means. The same conscience, the same devotion to humanity, the same science can direct these two peoples in their assumption and exercise of the great responsibility which has come to them.

The leaders of Russia have looked chiefly to France and Germany for their social theory, what they took in this way always being deeply modified in meaning by its Russian setting. They were influenced by the French Revolution and its rationalistic proponents, especially by Rousseau, whose early writings made a nihilistic attack upon civilization, with much nostalgia for the primitive habit of life which civilization had submerged. Civilization, he wrote, is just the successful effort of the few to enslave the many, by means of the violent theft of common property, the theft being then legalized by the institution of government. In his later writings, advocating political revolution against decadent feudalism, he still looked back to the small primitive community, closely bound by group association. There is, he wrote, in every community a common life and "general will," merging the individual in the group. He proposed to find expression of the "general will" in the vote of the majority, the infallible "voice of God." But would the vote of a majority to enslave or oppress a minority be the "voice of God"? And what does Rousseau's doctrine become when society is a great civilization? Hegel had no difficulty in perverting his predecessor's ideas to support reactionary absolutism. The "general will," he taught, is the "spirit of the nation," which comes to best expression in its aristocratic and intellectual élite. (It was Hegel's conception of the national will which the German Nazis dug up to justify their excesses.) And he proceeded to an ambitious "interpretation of history" which presented a panorama of nations and empires, each in its day the true expression of the *Weltgeist,* or "world spirit," imposing its form upon other peoples by war.

Marx undertook to turn Hegel's absolutism upside down and inside out. Influenced by French communists who ascribed the collapse of the French Revolution to a failure to follow up the equal distribution of political power with an equalitarian redistribution of economic power, he replaced Hegel's political "interpretation of history" with one which explained the course of political history as the effect of economic change. There is, Marx saw, a natural and basic economic progress, caused by improved methods of production; and it affects a continual shift of political power in society. There is consequent resistance to economic progress on the part of men whose political privilege depends on the established economy. The feudal nobility resisted the transition from agricultural to commercial economy; and the middle class or bourgeoisie, threatened by the transition to industrial economy which generates a large and powerful class of factory workers, now resists progress. He believed that the natural and therefore irresistible economic progress of society would "by dialectical necessity" sweep aside all political obstacles, and bring the workers to political power. That this "economic determination" of political and cultural history actually occurs is unquestionable; and Marx's attention to economic factors, with his perspicacious indication of their working in European history, made him the most important social analyst of his century. The Russian intelligentsia, aware that the political and economic backwardness of Russia were causally connected, found in Marx the first intelligible effort to explain this connection.

All contemporary social science is defeated by its failure to distinguish the three sorts of adaptation, and corresponding sorts of adaptability, which determine social history. Its failure of observation rests upon a deeper failure, the philosophical fallacy which would compel history into some structural straitjacket defined by a theory—a fallacy requiring the pretense that some formal or universal necessity determines the course of history, and dividing social scientists into two groups, the Marxist group which holds to the economic determination of all occurrence, and the more historical group which teaches the political determination of occurrence. There is no such general determination of natural occurrence, all that occurs being particularly necessitated. This is the basic dogma of empirical science, which holds all pursuit of general causation to be metaphysics and not science.

The duality of economic and political fact does not cover the social situation, and generates confusion of thought. The term "political" confuses social adaptation within the group with external adaptation among groups. The term "economic" confuses external adaptation to material nature with both of the other adaptations, external to other groups and internal to the one group. Thus social science becomes philosophical controversy, purely verbal, insisting that all three sorts of adaptation must be "really" just one sort. On the contrary, all three adaptations are most real, and quite disparate. Our problem is to bring all human groups into the one comprehensive association which is civilization. This requires new group adaptation, replacing or moderating the local group adaptations which now divide mankind into many groups. There must be political readaptation, i.e. progress of intergroup adaptation; and this requires, and is required by, economic readaptation, adapting the individual externally to nonhuman things. The human situation, in short, is always triadic, three-pronged, an eternal triangle, as is indeed any natural situation. Its triadic character reappears in every problem, because nature is always a plurality of groups in some larger context. Triadicity is written into the structure of nature. Yet it is discernible only in the progress of nature, where now one of the three prongs, and now another, is the apex of the triangle advancing progress. This ineradicable triadicity of nature was vaguely acknowledged in the theological dogma of the trinity. It was more explicitly acknowledged in the dialectical philosophy expounded by Hegel (trained, we should remember, in the theological seminary). In his "interpretation of history," he described how a "national spirit," advancing to expression and power, stimulates reactions in neighboring nations, leading to war and conquest. The rising "national spirit" is the *thesis,* the reaction of the neighboring peoples is the *antithesis,* and the conquest, with thesis absorbing antithesis, is the *synthesis.* He had found this notion of dialectical progression to be that of thought, an idea (thesis) in its variety of diverse applications (antithesis) gradually widening its content to become another idea (synthesis). He accordingly presented all progress as a progress of mind. Human progress is that of the *Weltgeist,* or world mind. But Hegel could not explain in this way the failure of empire, in which the risen nation, inciting reaction in neighbors, does not conquer and annex but is destroyed. His *dialectic* allows him to explain any history as dialectically necessitated, because he can say that the victor, whichever it were, evidently just had more "world spirit." He predicted that Germany, possessed of much "world spirit," would rise to world empire. The Germans took him at his word, attempted world conquest, and were destroyed.

Marx appropriated the notion of dialectical necessity; but he used it to support his economic "interpretation of history," the procession of dominant nations being replaced by a succession of dominant economic groups or "classes," each of which, in coming to power, establishes its appropriate political institutions and cultural forms. But behind this class dialectic, and responsible for it, Marx saw a necessary economic progress in production-method. He apparently conceived the progress to be due to the action upon man of the material environment, and to be beyond human control, the resistance by privileged classes working only to slow it up. The effect of dialectical necessity in Hegel is to generate an absolute faith in some national destiny. Its effect in the Marxist interpretation is to generate absolute faith in the destiny of the working class, or proletariat.

The scientist, and the society guided and informed by science, will discard "dialectical necessity," but retain the insight of dialectical philosophy into the triadicity of nature. In human progress, this appears in the three sorts of adaptation which condition persistence and promote or retard progress. The twentieth century has sufficiently invalidated the Hegelian dialectic, which brought Germany to complete ruin and all Europe to desolation. It is demonstrated that nationalism, however intense, cannot bring us to world civilization, but can and may destroy us all. The Marxist dialectic corrects this error and looks to the transcendence of national differences; but, literally taken, it would leave us wholly reliant upon "inevitable" economic progress, neglectful of the social or group readaptations which condition economic progress. Our purpose must be to *provide, by our creation of them,* those readaptations which will bring all human beings into social partnership, and outweigh all distinctions of nation, class, race, or other type. As a matter of fact, Russia in its application of the Marxist doctrine has taken the social economy emphatically under control. It uses group adaptation, implemented through government, to effect the transition to industrial eonomy. It adds Hegel to Marx, seeking to secure through its political adaptation the economic conditions of progress. But it should be clear that no system of political economy will of itself secure progress, and that no theory or doctrine which discovers only two factors, political and economic respectively, will give us understanding of social occurrence. This is demonstrated by the fact that social evolution leaves us today with two opposed ideals of what political economy should be.

Neither the United States nor Soviet Russia, it was noted, is practically confined by its formal theory. The United States makes political liberty paramount, implying that political liberty guarantees all values and secures progress; but in its practice it secures to the individual those individual economic powers, in private property, without which there could be no popular control of government. However, the idea that the equal distribution of political-economic power necessarily secures social progress is a fallacy, and a most dangerous one. Through political-economic power, the individual may exert political power to direct social progress; but there is nothing in the democratic constitution to prevent the individual from using such power to prevent progress, and even to destroy his society. There is nothing to prevent the dissolution of democratic society into a plurality of irreconcilable parties, bringing government to deadlock and the national economy to paralysis. In Europe such factionalism has developed, to undermine and to topple democratic governments. Individualist democracy conditions persistence and progress only where its members are so communally united that they seek the same sort of progress, the sole issues being whether the progress should be fast or slow, by one means or another, and under this or that administrative leadership. Democratic government is necessarily two-party government, the establishment of a third party serving notice of group maladaptation. This does not require the eternity of existing parties. It does require that there should be perpetual return to the two-party system, with one party in administration and another in opposition. The political constitution is and can be only the means by which the social adaptation of a group controls its other adaptive habit. The democratic constitution will serve a society so long as the individuals of that society place common objectives, necessary to the common good, above individual and minority-group interests. In other words, it will serve the individualist society which is devotedly communist in its concern for the common good.

The communist society, on the other hand, whatever its official dedication to the tenet of economic determinism, will always have to depend upon political machinery, securing its direction of the political economy. Moreover, in its endeavor to retain and to widen the adaptability which is a condition of every sort of progress, it will have to provide wide diversity of adaptive type, and be concerned to assure the largest freedom of individual development. Where individualist society must constantly be intent upon the common good, the communist society must constantly be intent upon the individual good. Each society must make good the one-sidedness of its system of government, by constant attention to the conditions of persistence and progress. These conditions can never be provided in their entirety by a form of political economy; but government can be used to support social progress by securing its economic conditions.

We conclude that the world civilization of the future not only can, but must, contain political economies of both sorts, individualist and communist. The progress required of us at this moment, as the social readaptation necessary to persistence and progress, and alternative to destruction or decay, is the recognition that individualist and communist societies are the vehicles of complementary insights. No *theory* can describe nature, because nature is finally the evolution, not the persistence, of structure. Similarly, no system nor institution can contain nature, because nature evolves. It was written in the bowels of nature that natural evolution should issue in two complementary types of political economy, individualist and communist. The agent of creation is a group of individuals. This group has secured persistence and progress by its continual change of type, by its progressive group readaptation. To fixate the political economy of man would be to destroy adaptability and stop progress. The group which sustains evolution must have variety of every type. The group which unifies the world and man must include and contain the United States and Soviet Russia, each with its distinctive system of political economy.

How is the step to world civilization to be taken? It is taken the moment these two peoples acknowledge each other as the complements of civilization, each necessary to civilization and *each necessary to the other*. Communism is needed because an individualist people, without constant reminder of the community and its needs, will disintegrate into a pursuit of individual ends, politically achieved. Individualism is needed because the communist society must be reminded that persistence requires adaptability and thus the widest diversity of type, which can be reproduced only through individuals. It is neither necessary nor desirable that civilization should become uniform in its political economy. On the contrary, it is necessary and desirable that there should be, and remain, diversity of political economy. That this diversity is dual

reflects the duality of nature, which is always and everywhere, eternally if that word has meaning, individual and
group. Neither Russia nor the United States can depart
from its basic principles of political economy. Neither
should do so. Each needs the other as it is. The world needs
both.

At peace, these two peoples will create a world. At war,
they will destroy a world. Neither individualism nor communism will be eliminated by anything that does not destroy the human race. Russia might be destroyed by war,
its government overturned. What would then happen? Its
vast territory would fall into political chaos, followed by
some form of feudal economy, slowly returning to a loose
imperial unity; but communism would work underground,
to arise in two or three generations more vigorous and mo-
mentous than before. A thousand years, not a half-century,
created the group adaptation which is communism. But
what will happen to the United States if Soviet Russia be
confounded? A world in turmoil will have to be policed;
and the United States, becoming a new imperial Rome, will
by imperialism abroad be corrupted at home, and lose all
liberty.

The reciprocal acceptance of each other by the United
States and Soviet Russia is not just a matter of words. It
requires an act of moral will, of reciprocal trust in spite of
radical difference. It requires large intelligence of each
other, not to be obscured by the stresses and strains of continuous diplomacy. It requires the will to day-by-day re-
adjustment. It requires largeness of heart, and absence of
fear. The people of the United States must understand that
Russia attempts to make up in a few decades what the West
achieved in as many centuries. The West, too, had its absolutism securing national solidarity, its persecutions and
purges, its "irreligious" disestablishment of churches, its

tumult by day and its terror by night. These things are now remote and forgotten; but they were, and had to be. Russia attempts exodus from medieval priestcraft, political reformation, and industrial revolution all together, *now*. Political absolutism has been, and for some time to come will continue to be, the alternative to chaos in Russia. Let this be understood! But let Russia know that a people which has come through these things does not return to them, nor try to repeat its own history. Government *of* the people *by* the people *for* the people shall not perish from the earth. It will not perish because two peoples exist, each to remind the other of the preposition which it is most apt to forget.

Let us turn from creed and doctrine to science, bringing intelligence and peace. All that is not science is infected with fear, and necessarily so. Since civilization began, man has known this conviction of sin which makes him dogmatic, violent, warlike, criminal, and cruel. What was his sin, what did he have to fear? His sin was to have left nature, his fear was of his own undirected power. He built himself false gods, theologies and ideologies which pretended to set forth the absolute, holy, omnipotent structure to which man must conform, on penalty of death or damnation. In this way he could serve, devote himself, forget his unnatural freedom, deny his power, pretend that destiny was in other hands. And since his idol was but clay, not life, myth and not truth, he could bear no denial of it, casting doubt; and those who would not bow, he slew. When there came congestion and unease, moral stress was intensified, and whole peoples went berserk, destroying until they were destroyed. Let us not deny that there has been and is this evil in the world, infecting human flesh and collapsing every civilization! Every religion and philosophy has sought escape from this evil, seeking its exorcism in a formula, finding a scapegoat to carry the sins of the world. Art was always tragic art, in tragedy following the unfortunates compelled by guilt to crime or suicide, in comedy displaying follies defiantly pursued on the brink of the abyss. Even beauty was the courage to take joy along with guilt.

Now let it be known that the day of guilt is over, that there is no sin and no crime to be evaded by scapegoat or creed. That sense of guilt was just the uneasy transition from animal to human estate. Man never left nature. He left only his dependence upon nature. He had still been hostage, dependent upon nature for his sustenance and life. He became governor of nature, friend and creator of nature. Any dependence of man upon nature became the dependence of nature upon man. Now, in this mid-twentieth century, the curse is lifted. Science instructs us that conscience is blessing, not curse, with no dreg of guilt. Conscience, become science, guides our creation of this world. Science, become conscience, tells us that creator we always were, doing in ignorance what we now intelligently do, openly, with gladness and good cheer.

Let us know this truth, accept our universe, and create with joy! Let there be no more war, but peace and good will in cosmos. We will not be Lucifer, turning from creative joy to cast down our office, consigning to perdition everything that is. We shall still be God, finding creation good, and bringing heaven and earth to greater splendor. There shall still be light! It is said! So be it! So be it!